Aristotle

PRAEGER PATHFINDER BIOGRAPHIES

CHARLES DARWIN

Pioneer in the Theory of Evolution

H. E. L. Mellersh

MOHAMMED

Prophet of the Religion of Islam

E. Royston Pike

Aristotle

FOUNDER OF SCIENTIFIC PHILOSOPHY

BENJAMIN FARRINGTON

PRAEGER PUBLISHERS
New York · Washington

BOOKS THAT MATTER

Published in the United States of America in 1969
by Praeger Publishers, Inc.
111 Fourth Avenue, New York, N.Y. 10003

Second printing, 1970

Library of Congress Catalog Card Number: 68–16211

Printed in the United States of America

Contents

1 Introduction   3

2 Personality and Background   11

3 At the Academy   17

4 Aristotle Leaves Athens   24

5 Aristotle Finds Himself   31

6 Aristotle Turns Biologist   36

7 Psychology   41

8 Alexander's Tutor   46

9 The Founding of the Lyceum   57

10 Aristotle's Logic   63

11 Physics and Metaphysics   71

12 Ethics and Politics   87

13 The Aristotelian Revolution   98

IMPORTANT DATES   111

SUGGESTIONS FOR FURTHER READING   113

INDEX   115

List of Illustrations

Socrates   5

Plato   8

Map of Greece   13

Philip II, father of Alexander   15

Map of the Troad and Lesbos   27

Domestic architecture in Aristotle's time   33

Alexander at the Battle of Issus   50

Head of Alexander   51

Map of Alexander's conquests   55

Aristotle's scheme of the four elements   73

Aristotle's picture of the cosmos   78

Dante's Christian version of the cosmos   82

Aristotle's ladder of nature   83

Bust of Aristotle   104

Aristotle

I

Introduction

Aristotle, pre-eminent both as a scientist and as a philosopher, has claim to the central place in the long history of Greek thought. As a doctor's son, he was born heir to a *scientific* tradition about two hundred years old. When, at the age of seventeen, he left Macedon for Athens to study under Plato in the Academy, his choice brought him to the fountainhead of European *philosophy*.

Philosophy is a necessary corrective and supplement to science. For two hundred years before Aristotle, Greek thinkers had wrestled with the problem of physical change. The outcome was the atomic system of Democritus, which matured about 420 B.C. As a scientific hypothesis, this system is so good that it was revived by the great modern chemist Dalton in the early years of the nineteenth century, and it is still an indispensable tool of thought. But it is not a philosophy. Philosophy tries to cover all reality, not particular aspects of it. Atom-

3

ism is a deterministic system explaining physical change as the result of mechanical causation. It cannot say anything about the freedom of the will or moral responsibility, except, by implication, to deny them. Of what use was this to Athens of the fourth century B.C.?

The very life-blood of Athens was politics. While physical science was developing elsewhere, Athens had displayed its genius in constitution-making. A rapid political evolution from monarchy to aristocracy and from aristocracy to democracy had made Athens politically conscious to a degree attained by no other ancient people and by few modern ones. The lawgivers, Solon and Cleisthenes, had taught Athens to think. But now democracy, which had exalted Athens to the pinnacle of power and leadership, had let her down with a crash. To pick up the pieces, it was of no avail to know how the dance of atoms in the void produces the changing spectacle of nature. The question was how men should behave in order to be happy.

It was in the effort to find the answer that Plato's Academy was born. The topics discussed in the Academy ranged far beyond politics in the strict sense. But the avowed aim of the Academy was to raise a new generation of men capable of saving Greece by political action based on a true and comprehensive philosophy.

The inspiration for this new approach to politics was derived from the life and teaching of Socrates. The personality of Socrates revealed to Plato the type of man on which a just State could be built. Socrates was not a writer. He stamped his personality on his age, and on all subsequent ages, by his manner of life and his conversation. A sociable and approachable man, staunch in the performance of his duties as soldier and citizen but adamant in his refusal to engage in an action he

Small figure of Socrates, from the British Museum. Copy of an original made early in the fourth century B.C., not long after his death. Socrates was thought to house a beautiful soul in an ugly body. (By permission of the Mansell Collection, London.)

thought wrong, he was predestined to martyrdom and did not shrink from it. Thus, committed to the assertion of a set of values beyond and above life, he preached the old doctrine of the immortality of the soul while giving it a new, intellectual content. For he defined virtue as knowledge, believing that no one could fail to practice virtue if he understood it. The good life was based on knowledge. In his own words, "The unexamined life is no life for a man."

In his quest for knowledge of the good, Socrates showed the stubbornness of his character and the rationality of his mind.

He sought intelligible definitions of the virtues and employed in the quest the method of induction. That is to say, various apparent instances of the virtue were proposed for discussion in the hope of arriving at an agreed definition. Aristotle, who was later to systematize this analytical procedure into what we now call the art of logic, gives credit to Socrates for originating the two major steps of induction and definition. It was through the example of Socrates that the word *dialectic*, which is the Greek word for conversation, acquired its meaning of a systematic search for truth by logical discussion.

These beginnings of a scientific approach to moral and political problems were taken up and developed by Plato into what is known as his Theory of Ideas, or Forms. This was an attempt to understand the worlds of both nature and society at a depth unplumbed by the older thinkers. Plato's model in this new approach was the already well-established science of geometry. A training in geometry, Plato thought, would best prepare the mind to grasp the underlying realities of the shifting appearances of things. Over the entrance to the Academy was carved the warning "If you do not know geometry, do not enter here."

Geometry took the place in Plato's educational scheme that was to be taken by logic once Aristotle had invented it. Geometrical truths, according to Plato, are innate in the soul. They cannot be gathered from sense experience, for we never encounter in nature a perfect straight line or a perfect circle. Rather, the imperfect and impermanent geometrical forms we meet here on earth merely serve to awaken in us the memory of the true Forms, which we knew before we were born but forgot at birth. Plato, of course, like Socrates, believed in the immortality of the soul.

We can apply this lesson to our endeavor to understand

virtue. The imperfect examples we encounter in our life on earth serve to awaken in us our forgotten knowledge of ideal Beauty, Truth, and Goodness. If we wish to discover the definition—that is, the essential nature—of, say, Justice, the only permanent foundation of the State, we shall find no example of it on this earth. The just State, like the perfect circle, exists eternally in some other world than ours, where the immortal soul had knowledge of it before its earthly pilgrimage began.

The mythical form of this effort of Plato's to express the inexpressible should not conceal from us the immensity of his advance beyond his predecessors. Let us turn to the world of nature for a further illustration.

The older thinkers had brought to light the difference between sense experience and knowledge. Our senses reveal to us a scene of perpetual change, of growth and decay, of coming-to-be and of passing-away. Knowledge aims at the permanent reality underlying the change. If we want to know what Man is or what Horse is, it is not sufficient to give a detailed description of one man or one horse. We want to arrive at the definition of Man that encompasses the innumerable individuals in the same class. The class is determined by the universal and permanent element shared by all the particular and perishable individuals we include in it. This is the Form, set forth in the definition. It is the intelligible reality of which the visible world is the transient image.

Plato gave these Forms, these intelligible and eternal realities, a separate existence in a world of their own. It was the natural step for a thinker who had clearly disentangled for the first time the universal from the particular element in things. But, as a theory of reality, it presented difficulties that Aristotle was later to expose.

Such, then, was the new kind of knowledge that Plato

Plato, from the Vatican Museum. (By permission of the Mansell Collection, London.)

sought to impart to a generation of men capable of catching a vision of the just city and going some way to realize it even on earth. We can easily understand how Aristotle was stimulated and molded by it. He chose to remain in the circle of the Academy for some twenty years—that is, until the death of his revered master. Only then, at about thirty-seven years of age, did he leave Athens and begin to develop an independent philosophical personality. Twelve or thirteen years of residence in various places away from Athens brought him to full maturity. In the last twelve years of his life he was head of his own school at Athens. The divergence then apparent between Plato's Academy and Aristotle's new foundation, the Lyceum, has led some historians to see Aristotle chiefly as the critic of Plato. A more just judgment sees him not only as Plato's most brilliant pupil but as his true sucessor. ←

The subtitle I have chosen for this book, the description of Aristotle as the "Founder of Scientific Philosophy," is a phrase coined by Werner Jaeger, one of his best modern interpreters. It serves to remind us that in Aristotle were united the two streams of thought originated by his predecessors. It also does justice to his claim to be the true heir to Plato's thought. For the Theory of Ideas, while it overemphasized the universal element in knowledge, was an indispensable step toward the goal of a scientific philosophy.

Bertrand Russell has recently set forth his view of Aristotle in another happy phrase. He calls him "the first professional philosopher." This description does not cut as deep as Jaeger's, but it is a neat expression of a difference between Plato and Aristotle, which is revealed throughout their careers. The difference is this: Plato was actively involved in politics in a way that Aristotle never was. Plato was a participant; Aristotle, a spectator. Plato, by birth and inclination a member of the ruling class of Athens, was precluded from choosing politics as a career by his disgust for both the contending parties; but, as we have said, he founded the Academy to train a new type of ruler. His philosophy was a return to politics by a roundabout route. Its ideal product would be what Plato called the philosopher-king, a combination of philosopher and ruler in one person.

Just about the time Aristotle joined the Academy, Plato, then sixty-one years of age, had responded to an appeal to go to Syracuse, the greatest center of wealth and power in the Greek world, to advise its tyrant, Dionysius II, and turn him into a philosopher-king. The project soon came to grief, but six or seven years later Plato went again on the same mission. This time he was away from the Academy for a whole year. Again he failed, and his life in Syracuse was not free from peril. His return to Athens was effected only with difficulty.

In another few years' time, a third opportunity presented itself for the Academy to play the leading role in directing the affairs of Syracuse. Plato was now too old to be actively involved, but his pupil Dion led a military expedition against the city, seized it, and declared it "free." His reward was a letter of congratulation from Plato. But when the inevitable opposition arose, Dion liquidated the trouble-maker and was then himself murdered, allegedly by another member of the Academy!

Aristotle stood aloof from these adventures, but he was not untouched by them. A dear friend (of whom more later) fell in the assault on Syracuse. But Aristotle was not on the expedition—not even as an army doctor. He had in him the makings of a professional philosopher, not a revolutionary politician. So he continued his studies. In his later thought on the subject of politics, the concept of the philosopher-king had disintegrated under the scrutiny of his analytical mind.

2

Personality and Background

An ancient tradition, possibly from an unfriendly source, says that Aristotle had spindle-shanks and small eyes, and spoke with a lisp. To compensate for these physical defects, he was notably well dressed. His cloak and sandals were of the best, and he sported rings. Presumably he was rich. His father was already dead when Aristotle came to Athens, but the family had property at Stagira. One use he made of his money was to begin the habit of collecting books. Plato, with a touch of contempt for his devotion to reading, called him "the mind."

Aristotle's father Nicomachus had been court physician to the Macedonian king Amyntas II. This no doubt meant that Aristotle was familiar as a boy with the court where he was to act in his forties as tutor to the future world-conqueror Alexander the Great. Pella, the new and beautiful seat of government of the Macedonian kings, lay on the river Lydias where it broadens into a lake. The site had been chosen for both safety and commerce. The river, after it issued from the lake, continued as a navigable waterway some miles down to the sea.

The connection with the Macedonian ruling house is an essential feature in Aristotle's career. It began when he was a boy, under Amyntas II; it was renewed in middle life, when Philip II invited him back to be tutor to Alexander; it persisted after Alexander's departure for the East. For then Aristotle returned to Athens under the protection of the Macedonian viceroy Antipater, who was his close personal friend and was to act as executor of his will. Aristotle was all his life the dependent of a territorial monarchy, not a member of the ruling class of an autonomous city-state.

The circumstance of his Macedonian birth brought Aristotle an experience different from what Athens had to offer. Athens, the home of democracy, but now politically on the decline, was the administrative center of a small territory. Its people prided themselves on being descended from the original inhabitants of the soil and were fiercely jealous of their political autonomy, the threat to which now came precisely from Macedon. Stagira, where Aristotle was born, was an insignificant Greek colony, one of the many hundreds of those in which Greeks lived among non-Greek peoples over whom they exercised control. It, and the other Greek colonies in its neighborhood, was surrounded by Illyrians and Thracians, still at the tribal stage of society. Here the Greeks were a dominant race in the midst of a simpler alien population. But the individual cities were not jealous of their political autonomy. They were all glad to look for protection to the Macedonian dynasty at Pella.

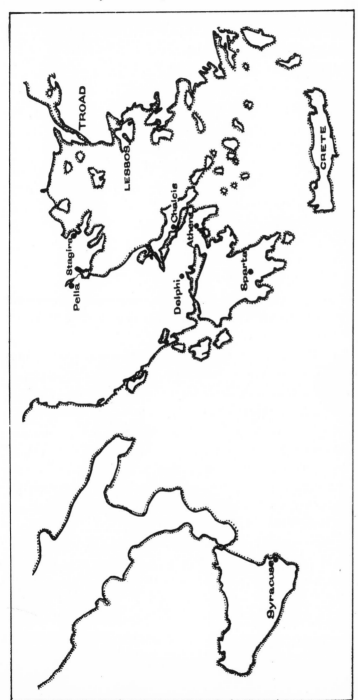

Sketch map of Greece, showing places mentioned in the text.

The Macedonians had only recently and grudgingly been admitted to the Greek family. This was in recognition of their services to the Greek cause in the Persian invasion of the early fifth century B.C. Once admitted, they undertook a policy of aggrandizement. By the gradual enlargement of the area under its control, the ruling family at Pella created something more like a populous modern nation state than the little independent city-states beloved by the older Greeks. This was but the preliminary to reducing all the Greek city-states to the status of local centers of administration in a Macedonian empire. This process was completed during the lifetime of Aristotle, and there is no reason to think he disapproved of it.

The richness of the soil of Macedon provided the economic basis for the execution of the political design. There were low-lying plains and lush river valleys shut in by wooded hills. The land was good for horses, cattle, sheep, grain, wine, and fruit. When the bounds of the kingdom had been extended to include the neighboring silver mines, there was an added source of wealth and power. The first Macedonian coins were minted before the middle of the fifth century.

Philip II, Aristotle's patron and father of Alexander the Great, well understood how to exploit these resources. He set to work to modernize his wealthy but backward country. It was a difficult task to imbue the different racial elements with a common loyalty toward the state. Philip was equal to it, and his instrument was the army. From the Greek cities, which fringed the seaboard with its hinterland of rich bottom plains and its opportunities for commerce, he drew his cavalry, which he honored by the title of his Friends. The Thracians and Illyrians, who were farmers and shepherds in the service of the Greek landowners, fought on foot. They were welded into the famed Macedonian phalanx with which Philip won

Philip II, father of Alexander, from a gold medallion. On the reverse, the goddess of victory in a four-horse chariot. (By permission of the Mansell Collection, London.)

his wars. Discipline and *esprit de corps* were set to do the work which might have been done by patriotism in a homogeneous population. With an army of this sort, drawn from a vastly more extensive territory than that controlled by any of the older city-states, Philip subdued Greece, and Alexander conquered the world.

Having considered what Aristotle owed to his country, we may conclude with what he owed to his father. As a physician, Nicomachus was a member of the guild of the Asclepiadae. These were the "sons" of Asclepius, the legendary founder and patron deity of medicine. Medicine at this time was traditional in certain families, being handed down from father to son by apprenticeship rather than by book-learning. Here in all likelihood Aristotle learned the fundamentals of that practical skill that he was afterward to display in his biological researches.

As an apprentice, he would have gone through a rigorous and varied training. He would have studied the role in therapy

of diet, drugs, and exercise. He would have learned how to
check the flow of blood, apply bandages, fit splints to broken
limbs, reduce dislocations, and make poultices of flour, oil, and
wine. Such, at least, were the skills of the trained physician.
We cannot be sure that Aristotle acquired them, but we do
know that medicine was studied in the Lyceum, and that
Aristotle, who later developed a distinct vein of snobbery,
thought that an educated gentleman should know medical
theory but should not practice.

3

At the
Academy

Plato called Aristotle "the mind." It was a justified tribute. But he might with equal justice have called him "the heart." If in the end Aristotle came to a fine balance between emotion and intellect, there was a time when it seemed that his feelings were the stronger.

A story is told of Plato giving a reading of his *Phaedo*. This dialogue purports to be the record of Socrates' last day. He has been condemned to death and is to drink the hemlock at sunset. His friends come to him in the morning and the immortality of the soul makes an appropriate subject for their last day's talk. Some of the argumentation is tedious; but the dialogue, together with the narrative portions, is moving and solemn in the extreme. However, as Plato read, his audience began to melt away till in the end Aristotle was left alone.

The anecdote is probably an invention, but it was invented to enshrine a truth. Aristotle was, in fact, spellbound by the Socratic doctrine of immortality as expounded by Plato. It did not simply interest him intellectually: It absorbed him emotionally. His earliest works, which were dialogues written when he was a member of the Academy, are obsessed, even to a morbid degree, with thoughts of the next world and the worthlessness of this one. These writings are all lost, though they had an enormous vogue in the centuries after Aristotle's death.

We have mentioned a friend of Aristotle's who fell in the assault on Syracuse. He was a young Cypriot called Eudemus, a man of high family, exiled for political reasons, and no doubt drawn to the Academy as much for its political orientation as for its philosophical doctrine. After Eudemus' death, Aristotle dedicated to his memory a dialogue on immortality which he called *Eudemus*.

The little work, of which fragments survive, opens a window into Aristotle's youthful mind. It tells how Eudemus, on a visit to Pherae in Thessaly—a visit, the story implies, not free from political intention—fell dangerously ill. In sleep, a beautiful youth appeared to him bringing three cheering announcements. The first was that he would soon get well; the second, that the tyrant of Pherae would soon meet his end; the third, that within five years of his recovery from his illness he would be restored to his own country. All went at first as the dream foretold. Eudemus got well, the tyrant was assassinated, and the fulfillment of the third prophecy was confidently awaited. But when the five years had passed, Eudemus, instead of being recalled to Cyprus, fell in the assault on Syracuse.

Brooding on his loss, Aristotle realized that their interpretation of the third promise had been superficial. When the vision

promised Eudemus a return after five years "to his own country" it did not mean Cyprus but the Other World, the realm
of the True, the Beautiful, and the Good. This was the culminating blessing that had been promised to Eudemus; for,
argues Aristotle, the old saying is true: "The best for man is
not to be born; the second best, to die as soon as possible." Life
in the body is not the true life of the soul, but a sickness for
which death is the cure. As in ordinary illness, the memory is
often impaired only to be restored when we return to health,
so in the sickness that is life the memory of the Ideal Forms is
destroyed but will be recovered when we die. Aristotle is still
a pure Platonist.

This way of consoling himself for the loss of a friend might
not seem to differ much from Shelley's *Adonais* or Tennyson's *In Memoriam*. There is, in fact, evidence of a very different attitude toward death. For instance, in a famous later
work, the *Protrepticus* or *Exhortation to Philosophy*, a work
so esteemed in its own age that it reveals Aristotle as one of
the founders of the religion of later pagan antiquity, Aristotle
develops the theme of life as a sickness of the soul. He recalls
the practice of Etruscan pirates who bound their living cap-
tives to dead bodies, matching them limb to limb, and so left
them to die. Such, says Aristotle, is the plight of the living
soul when harnessed to the body.

There are Platonic elements in Aristotle's mood, but the
pessimism is not Platonic. Plato's political bent kept him in
better balance; his life was a continuous endeavor to embody
the values of the eternal world in the earthly city. But Aristotle, in his early period, isolated the philosophy of Plato from
its political context. He took philosophy out of politics and
gave it a new function. He made it a substitute for political
activity, a withdrawal from the world, a personal effort to

perfect the soul by study and meditation while awaiting the release of death. In this sense he professionalized philosophy. It came easy to him to do so because he was, after all, not a citizen but a resident alien at Athens. It came easy also because the inevitable effect of the spread of Macedonian power was to destroy the political autonomy of the city-states and transform them into centers of local government, major questions of policy being reserved for the decision of the Macedonian overlords. To separate philosophy from politics had become a necessary division of labor.

This division was all the more necessary because a new and absorbing task had arisen to engage the attention of the philosophers. Among the more thoughtful of the Greeks, the gods-in-human-form of the popular mythology had begun to lose their authority. They were felt to be both childish and morally objectionable because of their licentious behavior. And now they had failed in a new way. They were but local gods with limited jurisdiction, and meanwhile, with the growth of communications, the world was becoming one. Gods were wanted whose authority would cover all men, gods seen of all and known of all.

These gods were found in the stars. The idea of the divinity of the heavens was not new; but now, with the rise of astronomy, the new religion was systematized and filled with a rich intellectual as well as emotional content. The hammering out of the main features of the new astral religion had been the serious preoccupation of Plato and his Academy in his last twenty years. This was the period of Aristotle's residence there, and he was one of the master spirits in the elaboration and propagation of the new faith.

Astronomy was, of course, an ancient science. In Mesopotamia and in Egypt, it had been cultivated for about two thousand years before the Greeks came on the scene. But here, as in many other departments of knowledge, the Greeks were pioneers as well as pupils. They were the first to imagine a geometrical model of the universe. We take this innovation for granted, and smile at the Greeks' geocentric universe because it is no longer ours. But the creation of the model was a far more revolutionary step than any modification which has been made in it since. The Copernican system, which is sometimes chosen as marking the beginning of modern science, was a trifle compared with the Greek achievement. The heavens had long been admired for their majesty, but now they were worshiped for their intelligibility. It was to this intelligible universe the Greeks gave the name of *Cosmos*. The word, a metaphor taken from daily life, meant order, regularity, decency, comeliness. Now, by the aid of geometry, order and harmony were disclosed in the celestial sphere on a scale undreamed of before. The religion of the Cosmos was ready to be born, though there were some birth pangs still to be endured.

The main obstacle to the birth of the new religion was the patent fact that order and regularity did not everywhere prevail. The chief sinners were those celestial bodies, the planets. "Planet" is the Greek word for "vagabond," and these celestial vagabonds were a thorn in Plato's flesh. They made it impossible to regard the visible heavens as a true Cosmos. This made Plato, in the *Republic*, which was written shortly before Aristotle joined the Academy, warn against putting the visible heavens in the first rank of divinity. "The starry heavens which we behold," he wrote, "are wrought upon a visible ground, and therefore, though the fairest and most perfect of visible things, must necessarily be deemed inferior far to the true motions of absolute swiftness and slowness, which are to be apprehended by reason and intelligence, but not by sight."

But during the last twenty years of Plato's life, through the genius of certain mathematical astronomers working in association with him, it was found possible to explain away the apparent irregularities in the planetary motions. They were interpreted as the resultants of a number of different motions all regular in themselves. The spangled heavens, the Cosmos, had proved to be a more intricate structure than had been supposed, but it did not transgress in any way the order, decency, and comeliness demanded of the Divine. Nothing any longer prevented the worship of the visible heavens. The time was ripe for the dethronement of the mythical gods. Cosmic religion was born.

In his last work, written just before his death, Plato made the new position clear. I compress his statement but keep to his own words: "A man may give what account he pleases of Zeus and Hera and the rest of the traditional pantheon. But we must insist on the superior dignity of the visible gods, the heavenly bodies. The neglect of the Greeks to pay proper honor to the heavenly bodies, the gods whom we all actually see, is inexcusable. They should be honored not merely by feasts on the calendar, but by setting ourselves to get a scientific knowledge of their motions and periods. Every true Greek should recognize the duty of prosecuting astronomy in a scientific spirit and cast off the superstitious fear of prying into the Divine. God knows our ignorance and desires to teach us. The study we require to bring us to true piety, which is chief of the virtues, is astronomy, knowledge of the true orbits and periods of the heavenly bodies. But it must be pursued in the spirit of pure science, not in that of Hesiod's farmer's calendar. Without this scientific knowledge a city will never be governed with true statesmanship, and human life will never be truly happy."

Such was the revolution of thought born in the Academy during the twenty years of Aristotle's stay. It was a complex and vast change of consciousness. It was a revolt against Greek tradition, but every Greek was asked to make it a matter of national pride to lead the revolt. It was not narrowly national, however, for it meant the acceptance of universal gods in place of Greek deities. It aims were religious, political, and ethical, but it sought to penetrate these three spheres with the scientific spirit. It meant a psychological revolution too, for the *psyche*, the life principle, was now thought to participate in the divine nature of the stars.

Such was the positive side of Aristotle's outlook on the world at this period of his life. The vitality of this religion is shown by its persistence. Kepler, one of the modern founders of astronomy, writes quite naturally: "We astronomers are priests of the highest God in regard to the book of nature." Wordsworth is quite close to Aristotle when he says:

> Our birth is but a sleep and a forgetting:
> The Soul that rises with us, our life's Star,
> Hath had elsewhere its setting,
> And cometh from far.

We all still feel a touch of the cosmic religion when we are lucky enough to escape the glare of city lights and find ourselves alone beneath the night sky.

4

Aristotle
Leaves Athens

For Aristotle, 348 B.C. was a black year. His native town, Stagira, offended King Philip, who razed it to the ground. Alexander, when he succeeded to the throne, rebuilt it to please his tutor—a proof, if one was needed, that Aristotle had not forgotten his grief at its fate.

But the same year brought a more personal grief, the death of Plato. Aristotle was an occasional poet, and some lines which he wrote in memory of Plato have survived. They are a philosopher's verses, deeply felt but preoccupied with the careful definition of what he found most admirable in Plato. Two phrases are particularly significant.

The first, which seems to rise out of the controversy that inevitably attends the passing of a great man, protests that Plato was "one whom it is not lawful for bad men even to praise." One senses the jealous championship of a disciple pained by the eulogies of the unworthy. The second makes a high claim for Plato with a meticulous concern to avoid exaggeration. Plato is described as the one "who alone, or first, among men revealed both in his way of life and in his formal teaching that to become good and to become happy are two sides of the same endeavor." "Now," adds Aristotle, for whom this lesson was a milestone in history, "no man can ever win this praise again."

On reflection, it is clear why Aristotle, in spite of the prosaic tone, feels obliged to say "alone, or first." It was Plato who made the breakthrough. None could rob him of this title to praise, though others might follow him. No subsequent criticism of Plato's opinions by Aristotle can outweigh this praise. That happiness and goodness are two sides of the same thing is a doctrine Aristotle later qualified but never abandoned. It remained to the end the inspiration of his work.

After Plato's death Aristotle left Athens. It is sometimes said that he did so in disgust at not being appointed to succeed him as head of the Academy, but this is an idle notion. The Academy, in the physical sense, consisted of a house and grounds owned by Plato. Aristotle, as a resident alien, could not legally have held the property; the ownership, and the headship with it, passed to Plato's heir, his nephew Speusippus. Thirteen years later, when Aristotle returned to Athens and opened his own school, the Lyceum, conditions were different. Athens was under Macedonian control, and Aristotle's path was made smooth by Antipater.

Meanwhile, Aristotle made a choice of residence that may seem surprising at first glance but is, on reflection, found to be most natural. He managed to combine a complete change of scene with remaining in the closest contact with the work of

the Academy. He crossed over to the Asiatic side of the
Aegean to the newly built town of Assos, where there was a
small branch of the Academy helping to spread Greek rule
and Greek philosophy on Asiatic soil. How Assos became for
a short while a center of light and learning is a curious story
only recently pieced together.

Plato had had two disciples at the Academy in Athens,
Erastus and Coriscus, who came from the town of Scepsis in
the Troad, in Asia Minor, not far from which Assos was to be
built. On the completion of their studies, after being imbued
with the doctrine of the philosopher-king, they found an un-
expected opportunity to put their theory into practice. In their
neighborhood was a Greek soldier of fortune. He had also, it
appears, visited the Academy, and he was now engaged in
carving out a little kingdom for himself in Asia.

This man, Hermias, who came from the neighboring town
of Atarneus, was of obscure origin. At some stage of his career,
he had had the misfortune to be made a eunuch; but eunuchs,
as Aristotle tells us, though they may acquire a feminine soft-
ness as well as a shrill voice, tend to grow strong and tall.
Hermias was strong and energetic. The fortune he had managed to scrape together as a banker or money-changer was for
him merely the means to an end. First he gained control of a
few villages on the slopes of Mt. Ida. Then (no doubt in return for a consideration) he secured from his Persian over-
lord recognition of the title of Prince of his little realm.

While thus proceeding steadily to extend his political and
military power, Hermias did not forget the impression he had
formed of the value of Plato's teaching. He accordingly ap-
proached Erastus and Coriscus for aid. They, in turn, ap-
proached Plato. By good luck, we possess the reply made by
Plato to assist the three of them in their decision.

Map of the Troad and Lesbos, scene of Aristotle's activity from 347 to
341 B.C.

His failure in Syracuse had not abated Plato's political zeal.
He urged the three to profit by the lucky chance of their being
neighbors. Hermias was to find the advice of the two young
men invaluable—of even more worth to him than a regiment of
cavalry and a mine of gold. Erastus and Coriscus, for their
part, were to remember that their sheltered life in the Academy
had in no way equipped them to deal directly with political
realities. They were to put themselves under the protection of
Hermias. It would be his part to assure them leisure for their
studies by meeting their material needs, and, in return, they

would make a philosopher of Hermias. They heeded Plato's words. Hermias settled down to study geometry and dialectic, and Erastus and Coriscus left Scepsis and came to live in his new capital of Assos in order to direct his studies. It is even said that, as a result of their joint efforts, a milder regime prevailed in the little kingdom.

This, then, was the milieu to which Aristotle transferred himself on the death of Plato. He left the original Academy only to go to its offshoot in Asia, and he brought with him his Macedonian as well as his Athenian experience. Nor did he go alone. With him went another Academician of note. This was Xenocrates, slow-witted but of great moral weight. "The one needs a spur," Plato is reported to have said, "the other a bridle." And again, in a moment of impatience, "See what an ass I am training to compete with what a horse!" But the horse and the ass had more sense than to compete. They combined their respective talents and pulled together in the new Academy.

Here they were soon joined by another man of a genius hardly less impressive than Aristotle's. This was Theophrastus of Eresos on the neighboring island of Lesbos. He too had been at the Academy, and he was one day to succeed Aristotle as head of the Lyceum. Hermias did not lack advisers. Could any other town on earth at that time have boasted such a concentration of talent?

It is to this period of Aristotle's life that the first twelve chapters of the Seventh Book of his treatise *Politics* belong. In them we find sketched the political ideals he held at the time when, with his other companions from the Academy, he was advising Hermias. In this sketch, the connection between philosophy and politics is clearly stated. The highest purpose of a city-state (*polis*) is to secure the conditions in which the minority who are capable of it can live the philosophic life. But this is only within the capacity of Greeks.

The inhabited earth, Aristotle explains, is divided among three types of men. To the west lie the Europeans. They live in a cold climate, and, while full of courage, are deficient in intelligence and aptitude for techniques; through their backwardness they have not been able to advance from the tribal to the political stage, and they are unfit to rule other peoples. To the east lie the Asiatics. They are intelligent and possessed of technical skills, but they lack spirit and are therefore subject and enslaved. The Greeks, who lie between, combine the good qualities of both. They have both intelligence and spirit; they are natural rulers. If they could achieve political unity they would rule the world.

The city-states, however, should individually be small in size, to enable all the citizens to take part in public life. A Greek elite alone should be citizens. They should bear arms in youth, govern in middle life, and fill the priesthoods in old age. The land should be owned by the citizens but worked by the non-Greek serfs of the territory. The necessary arts and crafts would be plied by slaves, the supply of whom (we learn elsewhere) would be recruited forcibly from among the tribal peoples. If the city-state was so situated as to need a navy, the men at the oars should be slaves; the fighting men, citizens.

This, of course, was the kind of regime introduced on a large scale in Macedon and imitated on a smaller scale by Hermias. The racial pride and slavery shock us, but if we wish to be just we must remember the historical conditions of Aristotle's age and seize his conception at its positive and progressive side. The ideal of civilization created by the Greeks had elements in it above what had elsewhere been achieved. Aristotle served this ideal with a passionate devotion. It was his weakness to suppose that the Greeks, who had created it, could alone be the bearers and beneficiaries of it throughout the confines of the habitable earth.

5

Aristotle
Finds Himself

Aristotle spent the years between 348, when he left Athens, and 341, when Philip invited him back to Pella, either in Assos or on the neighboring island of Lesbos. As his sketch of political society shows, he was at home in the spiritual atmosphere of these places.

Soon he found himself at home also in a more intimate sense. His patron Hermias turned out to be a man after Aristotle's heart, and Hermias had a niece, Pythias, his adopted daughter, who turned out to be a woman after Aristotle's heart. He married her, and she bore him a daughter, whom he called by her mother's name. In the treatise *Politics*, from which we have already quoted, Aristotle prescribes the ideal ages for marriage—thirty-seven for the man, eighteen for the wife. Since Aristotle was himself thirty-seven at this time, we can make a probable guess how old Pythias was. "As for adultery," says Aristotle in the same connection, "let it be held disgraceful for any man or woman to be found in any way unfaithful once they are married and call each other husband and wife." In his will, Aristotle orders, "wherever they bury me, there the bones of Pythias shall be laid, in accordance with her own instructions."

Unhappily, Pythias was not destined to a long life. After her death, Aristotle chose another mate, Herpyllis, who bore him a son, Nicomachus. She outlived him, and Aristotle made ample and considerate provision for her in his will, "in recognition of the steady affection she has shown me." On the whole we have evidence of the great personal happiness Aristotle found at Assos.

This personal happiness is reflected in his *On Philosophy*, the last and greatest of his literary works—the last, because from this date on his energies were to be devoted to research and teaching and the composition of the more technical treatises by which he is known to us; the greatest, by reason of the influence it exercised on the thought of later antiquity. It, perhaps more than any other single work, established philosophy as a profession.

About the same time, he composed a work, *On Kingship*, in which he firmly demarcates the function of the philosopher from that of the king. He altered Plato's dictum, we are told, for the better by teaching that "it was not merely unnecessary for a king to be a philosopher, but even a disadvantage. Rather a king should take the advice of true philosophers. Then he would fill his reign with good deeds, not with good words." Hermias must have been relieved by this dispensation! At the same time, the philosopher was assured of his independent role.

On Philosophy, pitifully scant as the surviving fragments of

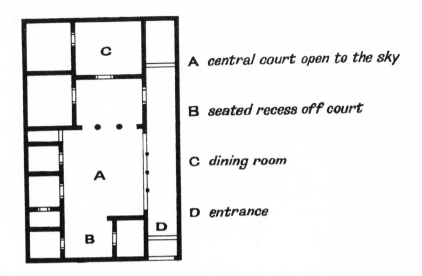

A *central court open to the sky*

B *seated recess off court*

C *dining room*

D *entrance*

Domestic architecture in the Greek world during Aristotle's time.

the work are, defines in a characteristic way the specific role of the philosopher. In it, Aristotle traces the order in which the various elements of civilization originate. There are five main stages, of which the culminating one is philosophy. (1) First, necessity compels men to devote themselves to the creation of utilities, without which they could not survive. (2) Next come the arts devoted to the refinements of life. (3) This stage is succeeded by the discovery of the art of politics, which is the prerequisite of the good life, as Aristotle conceived it. To the necessities and refinements of life it adds the knowledge of their proper use. (4) With the emergence of the well-regulated State comes the leisure for philosophy, which at first occupies itself with the material causes of existing things, as the older thinkers did. (5) Finally comes the shift from natural to divine philosophy, when the mind lifts itself above the material world and grasps the formal and final causes of things, realizes the intelligible aspect of reality and the purpose which informs all change.

Of course, this divine philosophy turned its eyes principally upward to the new astral gods. It will be remembered that Aristotle had lived in Athens through the long intellectual struggle to discover perfect order in the heavens. He had shared the relief of knowing that perfection was not to be confined to the mathematical abstractions, to which Plato had at first directed the attention of his pupils, but that the visible heavens themselves could be accepted as the embodiment of the Divine. His newly emancipated delight in the divine spectacle of Nature finds moving expression in *On Philosophy*. An eloquent passage has survived, and with it we shall conclude our chapter:

> Imagine a race of men living underground in rich and beautiful dwellings adorned with statues and pictures and all the appurtenances of the very wealthy, but knowing only by hearsay of the existence of a divine majesty and power; now suppose that the earth suddenly opened its jaws and let them emerge *into this world in which we dwell;* would they not be dumbfounded at the sudden sight of earth and sea and sky, the expanse of the cloudy heaven, the violence of the winds, the glorious sun in all its splendor and power spreading its beams to create our day, and the equal wonders of the night with its constellations; the waxing and waning of the moon, the rising and setting of the stars in their immutable courses; overwhelmed by all these sights, would they not believe that gods indeed exist and that these things are the work of their hands?

Contrast the enthusiasm of this Aristotle for the beauties of "this world in which we dwell" with the pessimism of the earlier Aristotle who was proclaiming that the best thing was not to be born and the second best to die as soon as possible. Consider this contrast, and measure the change which had come over Aristotle since he had settled himself in Assos. Was it due to a change of scene? Or to Pythias? Or to the new researches he now began to share with Theophrastus? Anyway it had happened: Aristotle had found himself.

6

Aristotle
Turns Biologist

After three years' residence at Assos, Aristotle moved to Lesbos with his friend Theophrastus, a native of that island. He settled in Mytilene, the capital city of Lesbos, where, in accordance with the missionary zeal that fired him and his friends, a philosophical circle was at once established.

But the change of residence produced, or favored, a shift of interest that became apparent at the time. He began to devote himself with passion to biological research, and the landlocked lagoon of Pyrrha in the center of the island has been identified as one of his favorite haunts. We may take this shift of interest as the result of his intense new delight in "this world in which we dwell," with its "earth and sea and sky." And soon the earth and sea began to claim the greater share of his attention. As a student of the heavens, Aristotle played the role of a systematizer and popularizer of other men's work. As a biologist, he was a pioneer.

It happens from time to time in the technical treatises that make up the bulk of Aristotle's works that we come upon an eloquent passage, designed, perhaps, for a public lecture or, if the audience was restricted to his regular pupils, to move them to the acceptance of a new and important point of view. Such was the beautiful passage we shall now quote. In it Aristotle is plainly faced with an audience accustomed to think of astronomy as far above other branches of natural philosophy, as indeed almost alone worthy of study. This, after all, had been Aristotle's own point of view. But now his opinion has changed. Biology now seems to him, if anything, more important than astronomy, and his concern is to coax his listeners to follow him along this new, unexplored, and even despised path of knowledge. He says:

> Natural objects fall into two great classes, the immortal ones that are without beginning or end, and·those that are subject to generation and decay. The former are worthy of honor and are divine, but less within the reach of our observation; all our speculations about them and our aspirations after knowledge of them can only in the rarest instances be confirmed by direct perception. But with regard to the plants and animals that perish, we are better off for coming to a knowledge of them, for we are inhabitants of the same earth. Anyone who is willing to take the necessary trouble can learn a great deal about all the species that exist. Both enquiries have their charm. Although in the case of the former we can achieve but little owing to their being out of our reach, yet the veneration in which they are held imparts to knowledge of them a degree of pleasure greater than appertains to any of the things that are within our reach, just as a lover would rather catch a fleeting

glimpse of his beloved than a complete view of other precious things.

But the latter, owing to our better acquaintance with them, have the advantage from the scientific point of view. Indeed their nearness to us and their kinship with us may be said to counterbalance the claims of divine philosophy. And, as I have already expressed my views on the former subject, it remains for me to treat biology, omitting nothing, so far as I can avoid it, however little or great be the esteem in which it is held. For though there are aspects of the subject that are unpleasant to our senses, yet from the theoretical point of view the sight of nature at her constructive task affords measureless satisfaction to those who are capable of coming to a knowledge of causes and who are philosophers by nature. For it would be irrational and absurd to take pleasure in images of natural objects, whether painted or modeled, because we detect the skill of the artist at work, and to fail to love still more the constructions of nature herself, always supposing that we **have the** capacity to understand causes.

Let us then not shrink like children from the investigation of the humbler creatures. In every natural object there is something to excite our admiration. You remember the story of Heraclitus, how when the strangers who wished to meet him halted in their approach on finding him warming himself by the kitchen fire, he bade them take heart and enter, saying: "here also there are gods." So we, too, must take heart and approach the examination of every living thing without reluctance or disgust, for in everything is some part of nature, some element of beauty. Indeed, it is in the works of nature most of all that we shall find purpose and freedom from indeterminacy; and the end for which the thing has been made supplies the place of beauty in a work of art.

Finally, if anybody despises the study of other living creatures as unworthy of attention, let him think the same of him-

self, for it is not possible without great disgust to contemplate
the elements of which mankind is made: the blood, the flesh,
the bones, the veins, and all such parts.

In the collected works of Aristotle, there are four separate
treatises on biology: *The History of Animals, On the Parts of
Animals, On Motion in Animals,* and *On the Generation of
Animals.* Taken together, they form the bulkiest group in the
collection. Altogether, some five hundred species of animals
are described, of which Aristotle had himself dissected specimens of fifty. The great topics discussed are (1) classification
by genera and species; (2) the distinction of the two meanings
of the term "parts" (i.e. whether the division is made according to materials, like skin, flesh, sinews, bone; or, according to function, like head, hand, heart, liver, and so on); (3)
differences in physiology, psychology, character, and habits;
and (4) the question of the appropriate *method* to be pursued
in natural science.

In his biological researches, Aristotle makes constant use of
a new type of causation. Like the old thinkers, he accepts the
play of mechanical causation in the inorganic sphere. A tile
falls off a roof and kills a man, but you do not blame the tile.
You do not suspect it of any intention. But a plant or an animal, which grows to maturity, passes through various stages,
and reproduces itself, seems to be guided by some *aim*, to be
pursuing some *end*. In attempting to understand this process,
Aristotle speaks continually of Nature's *intention*. If you burn
an acorn, you destroy it in a mechanical way; but if you give
it a chance, it turns itself into an oak. Here a new kind of
cause comes into play. The *aim* of the acorn, or of nature in
making an acorn, seems to be to make an oak. To admit the
existence of such ends or aims in nature is to argue teleologi-

cally (Greek *telos*, an end) or to admit the idea of a *final* cause (Latin *finis*, an end).

The employment of this type of causation by Aristotle has been much criticized in modern times; and, indeed, if teleology is used as a substitute for observation, the criticism is deserved. If we should say that man has been given hands in order to play the violin, we get things upside-down. Every natural organ develops a variety of functions that seem to be the result of the existence of the organ, not the cause. At the same time, Aristotle was quite right in seeing a degree of "finality" in nature; his only fault was that he sometimes tended to impose it on nature rather than to find it there by genuine research. But, on the whole, teleology with Aristotle was not a substitute for observation, but a most valuable concept for coordinating the results of his researches. Thus, confessing his ignorance of the mode of generation of bees, Aristotle writes: "The facts have not yet been sufficiently established. If ever they are, then credit must be given to observation rather than to theories, and to theories only in so far as they are confirmed by the observed facts."

Such is the manner and the temper of this great collection of biological works. It resulted in a classification of living things, a *scala naturae*, not superseded till the time of Linnaeus. One understands the often quoted remark of Darwin: "Linnaeus and Cuvier have been my gods; but they were only children compared to old Aristotle."

7

Psychology

The radical change of view on the nature of the soul, and more particularly on the relation of the soul to the body, that Aristotle now underwent arose naturally from his researches into plant and animal life. We know how fervently he had embraced the Platonic conception of the soul as an immortal visitant temporarily resident in the body, and connected with it only accidentally and extrinsically. Indeed, for Aristotle, life, or the residence of the soul in the body, had been equated with a sickness of the soul, a sickness for which death was the only cure. In this way, he had tried to console himself for the death of his friend Eudemus.

Now Aristotle's thoughts take a new turn. He subjects the concept of soul (*psyche*) to a searching new analysis. *Psyche* was, for the Greeks, what distinguished organic from inorganic matter. It was the life-principle. From this point of view, plants are credited with a simple form of soul, characterized by the faculties of nourishment and growth and reproduction. To these, the animal soul adds the faculties of sensation and locomotion. To these, man alone adds reason. Now, obviously, the psychic faculties of nourishment, growth, reproduction, sensation, and locomotion are inseparable from the body. But how does the matter stand with regard to reason? Aristotle gives the answer in his own words, in his work *On the Soul:*

> A problem arises in connection with the states of the soul. Are they all shared with the body, or is any one of them peculiar to the soul? The answer is all-important but not easy. In regard to the great majority of these states it seems plain that the soul neither suffers nor acts without the body. I mean when we are angry, or elated, or experience some want, or, generally speaking, have any sensation. Thinking seems a possible exception. But if thinking is a kind of imagining, if it cannot be done without mental images, then this too is impossible without the body. Only if we could detect some activity or affection of the soul confined to it alone, could the possibility of a separate existence of the soul arise. If there is none, it is impossible. And this seems to be so, for all the states of the soul, self-assertiveness, tenderness, fright, pity, boldness, not to speak of joy, love, and hate, all imply an associated state of the body. . . . We conclude that all affections of soul are inseparable from the material substratum of animal life.

It is goodbye, therefore, it seems, to all the argumentation with which Aristotle had tried to make life bearable when he wrote *Eudemus* and *Protrepticus*. Aristotle has, however, spoken of a possible exception to the general law of the interdependence of soul and body, and we must now inquire what this may be. It involves him in an emphatic distinction between soul and mind.

Having spoken of the various affections or states of the soul, Aristotle proceeds:

> With the mind it is different. It seems to be an independent substance lodged within the soul and incapable of destruction. If it could be destroyed old age would blunt and destroy it. But what happens to the mind in old age is just what happens to the sense organs. An old man, if he had a good eye, could see as well as a young one. The incapacity of old age is due not to what happens to the soul but to what happens to the body, as when a man is drunk or ill. So in old age the intellectual capacity declines only because of the decay of some other internal part. Mind itself is impassible. Thinking, loving, and hating are affections, not of mind, but of that which has it. Mind is no doubt something more divine and impassible.

The originality of these views is very great but does not, of course, preclude a debt to his predecessors. The Pythagoreans had long ago recognized plant, animal, and rational elements in the soul. There is a debt also to Plato, for Aristotle now defines the soul as the Form of the body, and the body as the Matter of the soul. But he denies what Plato asserted: that the soul is only accidentally and extrinsically connected with the body. For Aristotle now, the immortality of the soul, or Form, resides only in the species, but the individual is perishable. His view of Nature is that echoed by Tennyson, when he says of her,

> So careful of the type she seems,
> So careless of the single life.

But, apart from the persistence of the Form in the human type—a persistence common to all the Forms found in nature

—the soul partakes of immortality in another way. Insofar as that part of the soul which is called mind (*nous*) is able to lift itself up to the level of pure thought, that is, insofar as it becomes fully conscious of itself as a rational being, it then shares in the nature of the divine, rises above time, and partakes in eternity.

This concept has also its ethical side. It is the duty of man, says Aristotle, "to be immortal to the extent that is allowed him." This may seem a rarified conception, but it is inescapable. None of us feel that the whole meaning of our life is included within the biological definition of life. We have values that go beyond life and we try to act in accordance with them. In other words, we try to be immortal insofar as we are able.

At this stage of his development, Aristotle had attained the stature that makes him one of the foundation figures of European civilization. "What we nowadays mean by Europe," wrote Madariaga, "is above all a conscious (and even self-conscious) mind, capable of a continuous and ordered effort towards the understanding of the universe." It is for this ideal of civilization that Aristotle now consciously stands as he endeavors to develop the thought of the Academy and plant it in new centers like Assos and Mytilene. Still larger opportunities were just about to open before him. We shall reserve them for our next chapter. Meanwhile we may pause a moment to reflect on the significance for the future of what was then taking place.

"It was not the outer fabric of a future European civilization," writes Owen Barfield in his *History in English Words*, "which the Greeks were building up, but the inner world of human consciousness. They were helping to create our 'outlook.' The language which is used by the theologians, philosophers, and scientists of Europe was the gradual and painful creation of the thinkers of ancient Greece. Without that language the thoughts and feelings and impulses which it expresses could have no being."

8

Alexander's Tutor

In 341 B.C., when Aristotle was forty-three and Alexander was a boy of thirteen, Philip II invited the famous philosopher to Pella to act as tutor to the future world-conqueror. What were the motives that prompted Philip to this choice? Some of them are obvious. Aristotle was now the leading intellectual figure in Greece. Moreover, he was a Macedonian whose father had been family physician to Philip's predecessor on the throne.

So far, all is clear. But we must remember that Philip was not principally concerned with honoring the first philosopher in Greece. His task was to find the most suitable tutor for his son, whose future role as the military leader of the now united Greek world against the Persian Empire was already determined. Was Aristotle the obviously right choice for this par-

ticular post? What testimonials to his suitability could Philip
hope to have?

In this matter it is difficult not to suppose that Philip had
taken Hermias into consultation. The ground was already being prepared for the invasion of Persia. The little kingdom of
Hermias provided a bridgehead in Asia for the Macedonian
assault. Hermias, for his part, needed the protection of Philip.
A secret understanding already existed between the two men,
which was soon to leak out with tragic consequences for
Hermias. Such being the relationship between Philip and
Hermias, how can we suppose that, when Philip chose the son-
in-law and close friend of Hermias to be tutor to his son, he
had not sought from Hermias confirmation of his fitness for
the job? If consulted, what answer could Hermias have made
other than that his son-in-law was not only the greatest philosopher of the age but also passionately convinced that it was
the mission of the Greeks to rule the world if only they could
achieve political unity?

Aristotle's behavior in the tragedy that swiftly ensued bears
out this view. A year after Aristotle had gone to take up his
duties in Pella, suspicion of the existence of a secret treaty led
the Persian military commander to seize the person of Hermias.
He was taken to the Persian capital for interrogation under
torture and, on steadfastly refusing to speak, was put to death
by crucifixion. Granted the expression of a last wish before
execution, he is reported to have said, "Inform my friends and
companions that I have done nothing unworthy of philosophy." His identification of himself with the philosophical
circle at Assos is as noteworthy as his courage.

When these incidents became known, the anti-Macedonian
party at Athens, led by the great orator Demosthenes, de-
nounced the villainy of Hermias. The Macedonian party, with

Aristotle at their head, sprang to his defense. A cenotaph was consecrated to Hermias' memory at Delphi, the religious center of the Greek race. For this, Aristotle wrote the dedicatory epigram.

But, in addition to this identification of himself with a public grief, Aristotle felt the need of a more personal expression of his passionate admiration for his friend and father-in-law. He composed and published a poem more remarkable even than the one he had written for Plato. It celebrates Hermias as the exemplar of a type of heroic virtue issuing from the pursuit of philosophy, and it has given Aristotle his place among the minor poets of Greece. Here it is in prose:

> O Virtue, to which the race of men cannot attain without much toil, thou art the fairest prize of life. Such is thy beauty that for thy sake even death is an envied lot, death and the endurance of vehement invincible pains. Thy spell over the soul is stronger than life; it is a joy stronger than gold, or the lure of delight, or downy-eyed sleep. For thy service lived Heracles, son of Zeus, and Leda's twins, making of their many sufferings a witness to thy power to beget heroic deeds. Yearning for thee Achilles went down into the grave, down went Ajax yearning. And now for thy beauty's sake the son of Atarneus has made desolate the sun's beams. Therefore is he become a theme for heroic song; and the Muses will keep his name alive, the daughters of memory who uphold the reverence of Zeus, the god of friendship. Zeus keeps bright the reward of those whose love is faithful to the death.

This poem was written when Aristotle had already been installed at Pella for a year as tutor to Alexander. It can, therefore, with perfect justice be read as a revelation by Aristotle of the principles that guided him in his endeavor to form the mind and character of his charge. He was, like Hermias, to be

a hero of the old epic type enlightened by the latest achievement of Greek civilization, philosophy.

There is an important distinction between this ideal and the
older Platonic one of the philosopher-king. Aristotle has been
called the philosopher of common sense, and a certain practical wisdom distinguished him from Plato in his dealings with
men of action. When Plato went to the court of Dionysius at
Syracuse, his efforts were apparently mainly directed to teaching the busy ruler and his entourage the basic principles of
geometry. Antiquity made merry with the scene. Plutarch
describes the courtiers enthusiastically inscribing their circles
and triangles on the sanded floors until "the whole palace was
a whirl of dust." Aristotle, as we have already seen, had
exempted the ruler from specializing in philosophy. In his
scheme of studies, poetry, not geometry, took pride of place.

This was a revolutionary departure from Platonism. Plato's
quarrel with the poets is a familiar theme. It embraced both
epic and drama, Homer as well as Aeschylus, Sophocles, and
Euripides. Aristotle's elevation of poetry to a key role in education is therefore an important element in his radical revision
of the Platonic system of values. If he had shared Plato's dis-
trust of poetry, Aristotle would not have been a fit tutor for
Alexander.

Plato's quarrel with the poets may be considered on three
grounds. His first objection to poetry was its *unreality*. For
him, the world of Ideas was the true reality; the world of
nature and of man was but an imperfect copy of the true
world; the poets were doubly removed from truth because
they could at best produce no more than an imperfect copy of
an imperfect copy. The whole basis of this objection is removed if one follows Aristotle in denying the separate existence of the world of Ideas and in teaching that the Ideas only

Alexander at the Battle of Issus. Detail of a mosaic from Herculaneum, copied from an original painting of the fourth century B.C. (Naples, Museo Nazionale. Photo Anderson-Viollet.)

exist as embodied in the world of nature and of man. From this eminently sensible point of view, there is no reason why the poet should not be as successful as the scientist in penetrating behind the appearances to the reality. Poetry was for Aristotle not the enemy of philosophy but akin to it. He calls poetry "more philosophical than history."

Plato's second objection is to the emotional appeal of poetry. This objection is made in the name of reason. An individual, or a city, was well ordered when reason was in secure control of the emotions. The poets play upon the emotions, exercise them, give them free reign, and thus threaten the overthrow of reason. Aristotle, for his part, took the view that there can

Head of Alexander after
Lysippus, his official sculp-
tor. (By permission of the
British Museum.)

be no true education without an appeal to the emotions. A
good man is not a man without feelings but a man with dis-
ciplined feelings, not a man with atrophied emotions but with
strong emotions directed toward the right objects. Man
should not be regarded as a battleground between reason and
emotion. Rather, his emotions, through training in the imaginary world of literature and art, should be brought by habituation to harmonious cooperation with reason.

Plato's third point touched the dangers involved in the great
dramatic festivals. Here the poet addresses himself to the people at large, to the undisciplined crowd, to women and children; poetry's false values are offered with specious allure to

the uneducated multitude. This Plato thought utterly mischievous. Speaking as a lawgiver both in the *Republic* and the *Laws*, he urged that the poets should be banished from the ideal city as dangerous threats to the rule of law. Aristotle ignores this imaginary danger, treating pleasure in the arts as both natural and wholesome and insisting that intellectual understanding is not everything. The fear and pity roused by the tragedian's art have a purifying effect on the emotions. So, also, the business of the mystery religions is not to *teach* the initiate but to make him *feel*. In all this, Aristotle avoids contradicting Plato; he contents himself with stating his own very different conclusions.

These views of Aristotle's, which are found in his *Poetics* and scattered elsewhere through his writings, save us from being surprised that Homer played a key role in Aristotle's instruction of Alexander. The *Iliad* became Alexander's favorite book. He drew inspiration from the deeds and character of Achilles, whose remote descendant he liked to imagine himself to be. No sooner had he crossed the Hellespont at the start of his Oriental wars than he sought out the tomb of Achilles and placed a wreath upon it, while his friend Hephaistion garlanded the grave of Patroclus. Alexander and Hephaistion thus symbolized their intention of resuming on a vaster scale the older expedition against Troy. All this was in line with the thought of his tutor, with his conviction of the fitness of the Greeks for empire and his assertion that the philosophically trained Hermias was a genuine modern embodiment of the antique valor of an Ajax or Achilles.

Experience was, however, to make Alexander in one important point wiser than his tutor. Aristotle, with his fixed conviction of the superiority of Greeks over Asiatics, instructed Alexander to keep the barbarians (i.e. non-Greeks) in their place. He was to act as *leader* to the Greeks, as *master* to the Asiatics. The Greeks could be friends and kinsmen; the barbarians were to serve on a lower level, like animals or plants. The barbarians were to be the creators of the material goods without which a city cannot exist; citizenship was for Greeks alone, for they alone could aspire to the spiritual values which the city existed to foster and preserve.

Such were the implications of virtue (*arete*) as Aristotle understood it, but wider experience brought Alexander to a more sensible view. He sensed, as Aristotle did not, the unity of all mankind; and he decided, in spite of Aristotle's advice, to promote a physical intermixture of Greek and barbarian. He himself chose a wife from the Persian nobility, forced his high-ranking officers to do the same, and encouraged his troops to contract mixed marriages—believing it better, as many of the next generation of philosophers also did, to draw a distinction between virtue and vice rather than between Greek and non-Greek.

Nor, unhappily, was this the only cause of friction that arose between tutor and pupil. Aristotle had a nephew, Callisthenes, whom tradition reports to have been an intellectually able but practically foolish man. He was Aristotle's collaborator in a most interesting piece of research he undertook at this time. For Aristotle, it is not too much to say, was the real founder of Greek scholarship. At this time, he compiled a list of the victors at the Pythian Games. Since the Games were among the great national festivals that united all Greeks, this was a contribution of the first importance to the cultural history of Greece. It was followed by similar researches whenever the chance arose. Thus, he also compiled a list of victors at the Olympic Games. More significant still was his collection of the official records of the plays produced at the annual dramatic festivals at Athens.

But these later enterprises lacked the helping hand of Callisthenes. For Callisthenes was attached in the capacity of historian to the great company of learned men that Alexander took with him on an expedition which was intended as much to disseminate the culture as the military might of Greece. Here, after some years in which he successfully exercised his function of historian, Callisthenes imprudently decided to take his stand on a matter of policy in which he disagreed with his leader.

Alexander seemed to his Greek followers to be assuming more and more the character of an Oriental despot. The time came when he demanded that obeisance be made to him, and the resistance of Callisthenes to this demand involved him in suspicion of being implicated in a plot against Alexander's life. He was condemned and executed, and a breach opened between Aristotle and Alexander, which time was powerless to heal. In a way, the incident was more tragic than the fate of Hermias. That was inflicted by an enemy and resisted with heroic fortitude. But when his pupil executed his nephew on a false charge originating in a corruption of Greek ideals of kingship, what crumb of comfort could Aristotle find?

These events occurred after Aristotle's return to Athens. A word or two more will complete the account of his years in Macedon. It seems that when Aristotle first acceded to Philip's invitation to supervise the education of Alexander he resided, perhaps for a period of three years, at the court. But when Alexander, now approaching the ripe age of seventeen, was appointed co-regent with his father, Aristotle withdrew to his paternal property at Stagira. He had the company of Theo-

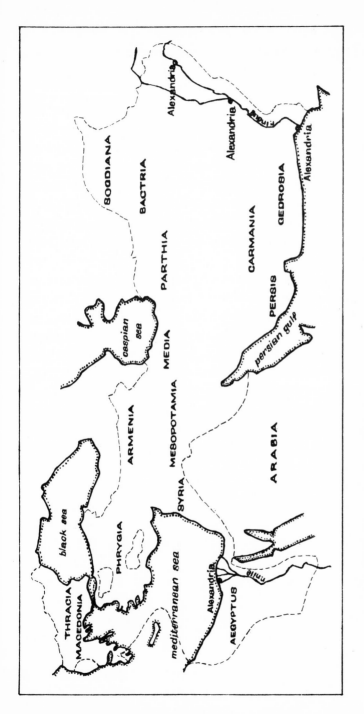

Sketch map of the extent of Alexander's conquests. Alexandria on the Nile was his greatest foundation, but there were at least a dozen other cities of the same name among the scores he founded. The sites of three are marked on the Indus.

phrastus, who had also acquired property there, and very probably of other old pupils of Plato as well. Finally, when Alexander ascended the throne, he gratified his tutor by re-building the town of Stagira which Philip had destroyed. Aristotle experienced the ups and downs of living in dependence on the great.

9

The Founding
of the Lyceum

Aristotle was near fifty years of age when, in 335 B.C., he returned to Athens to open his own school. The Macedonians were now the masters and unifiers of Greece, and Aristotle was the protégé of the Macedonian court. His closest personal friend was the Macedonian viceroy Antipater, whom Alexander, on his departure to the East, left behind to take charge of the affairs of Greece. Aristotle opened his school in the buildings attached to a wrestling school called the Lyceum, which was situated on a plot of ground consecrated to the service of the god Apollo Lyceus. The plot of ground was surrounded by a colonnade (*peripatos*) from which the school derived its familiar designation, Peripatetic.

It is difficult to imagine that a resident alien, like Aristotle, could have acquired the right to use the site without the support of the viceroy. The new school, of course, began and continued in a certain degree of rivalry with the Academy. That it was a friendly rivalry we may be sure, since the Academy was now under the headship of Aristotle's old colleague Xenocrates, who had gone with him twelve or thirteen years before to Assos.

The rest of Aristotle's life (he died at the age of sixty-two) was spent at the Lyceum. After his death, the school continued to flourish under the headship of his friend Theophrastus, until the Macedonian dynasty of the Ptolemies in Egypt decided to make Alexandria the chief seat of learning in the world. The Lyceum was then not formally closed, but its teaching personnel and its effects were in the main transferred to the Museum at Alexandria, with its twin branches of scholarship and science. The Museum was the Lyceum reborn. The spirit of Aristotle, if not Aristotle himself, presided over it. If we might use a modern industrial analogy, the Lyceum was the pilot plant for the Museum.

The Lyceum, then, was the pathfinder, the breaker of new ground. Its pioneering character explains to us the character of the Aristotelian *corpus*, which is neither like the dialogues of Plato nor like the orderly succession of textbooks which later streamed out from the Museum. At the Lyceum, a new method was being forged, and its activities were primarily research and teaching; and it is the primacy of research and teaching that explains the character of the written work surviving from the Lyceum. What survives from Plato's Academy is his published dialogues; we have only the scantiest evidence of the character and content of his oral instruction. With Aristotle, the situation is reversed. So long as he was a member of the Academy, he too wrote and published dialogues, which have all perished. The writings of his that we do

possess are precisely what is absent in the case of Plato: They
are the actual record of his teaching in the Lyceum.

On the other hand, in the Museum the production of textbooks was brought to perfection. Euclid's *Elements of Geometry* is the most celebrated but by no means the only surviving
example of this class. It was an achievement of the highest
order, rendered possible by Aristotle's work, but it was not
that at which Aristotle aimed. His writings all have, in greater
or lesser degree, the character of works in progress. They are
his lectures or lecture notes. Even the arrangement of the
corpus is the work of his editors. It is true that the order is to
some extent imposed by the nature of the contents. Logic is
regarded by Aristotle himself as a preliminary discipline, a
propaedeutic, and it naturally is placed first. But this has
nothing to do with the order of composition, and it has proved
impossible to determine this order.

At first sight, it seemed an easy problem. If one treatise refers to another, then surely we may conclude that the one
referred to was written first. But further examination shows
that if A refers to B, so also does B to A. The cross-references,
therefore, which are abundant, prove nothing as to the order
of composition. On the contrary they show that all the subjects were developing simultaneously under Aristotle's hand
in the course of his research and teaching. All continued until
his death to be subject to revision and amplification. This conclusion accords with their spirit. They are not dogmatic but
are testimonies to a rapid advance of knowledge on many different fronts.

The story of the survival of this unique *corpus*—unique in
revealing the growth rather than the consolidation of the new
mentality that was taking shape—is a curious one and this
seems the moment to relate it.

On the death of Aristotle, Theophrastus, the new head of
the school, inherited the manuscripts, and in turn he be-
queathed them to one Neleus, the son of his colleague Coriscus, with whom he had worked in the old days at Assos.
Neleus took the writings for safekeeping to the family home
in Scepsis. Some decades later, the Attalid dynasty of the
kingdom of Pergamum, which was endeavoring to found a
new center of learning to rival the Museum of Alexandria, was
on the prowl for books. The descendants of Neleus, wishing
to conceal their treasure from the prying eyes of the agents of
Attalus, hid the priceless manuscripts in a cellar.

There they escaped detection but not decay. They moldered
in the damp and dark until about 100 B.C., when they were
sold to an Athenian bibliophile, Ampelicon. He conveyed
them to Athens and attempted an edition, which did not succeed as well as might have been hoped in filling the gaps that
time had made. Then, in 86 B.C., Sulla captured Athens and
carried off the writings to Rome as part of the spoils. There
the first scholarly efforts to edit and interpret the collection
began. At about the same time began the decline of interest in
the earlier works. To Cicero, who was a young man when the
corpus arrived at Rome, Aristotle still meant only the literary
dialogues written in the Academic period. But his was the last
generation for which this could be true.

It has been questioned whether this romantic tale of the loss
and recovery of Aristotle's writings can be taken as true. Almost certainly it is true, but it is not the whole truth. If we
think of all the men who were trained at the Lyceum during
the twelve years of Aristotle's headship and the much longer
period—some thirty-five years—when Theophrastus was head,
it is impossible not to believe that in some shape or other the
main doctrines of Aristotle's system were readily accessible in

Athens to any interested inquirer. The history of the two new schools that sprang up in Athens while Theophrastus was alive and teaching is proof enough. Neither the Garden, the school of Epicurus, nor the Stoa, the school of Zeno, is intelligible except on the assumption that they were well informed of Aristotle's teaching on those aspects of philosophy that particularly interested them.

But when Theophrastus had died and the Aristotelian *corpus* had been carried off to Scepsis in the Troad, it is altogether probable that for two hundred years no complete Aristotle was anywhere accessible, except to the mice and spiders in the cellar where the work lay hidden. From 287 B.C., when Theophrastus died, until 50 B.C., when Andronicus produced the first edition of the *corpus* in Rome, Aristotle, except for his early literary works, was "out of print."

It will be convenient now, before we proceed to our brief discussion of the contents, to set out in tabular form what the *corpus* is all about. This can most conveniently be done by listing the various treatises as they appear in the twelve large volumes of the translation issued by the Oxford University Press between 1928 and 1952:

Volume I. Logic. This consists of six treatises. (a) The Categories—or the various ways in which a thing can be said "to be." (b) On Interpretation, or the doctrine of Propositions. (c) and (d) The Prior and Posterior Analytics, or the discussion of the Syllogism. (e) The Topics, or rules for logical arguing. (f) Fallacious Refutations, and how to expose them.

Volume II. (a) Physics (in eight books). (b) On the Heavens (four books). (c) On Coming-to-be and Passing-away (two books).

Volume III. (a) Meteorology (four books on the phenomena of the region of the sky below the Sun, Moon, and stars). (b)

On the Soul (three books on psychology). (c) Short Treatises on Nature, dealing with sensation and the sensible, memory, and the power of recall, sleep, dreams, divination in sleep, length and shortness of life, youth and age, life and death, respiration.

Volume IV. The History of Animals (nine books).

Volume V. (a) On the Parts of Animals (four books). (b) On Motion in Animals and their mode of progression. (c) On the Generation of Animals (five books).

Volume VI. Short treatises on Colors, Sounds, Physiognomy, Plants, Marvels, Mechanics, Indivisible Lines, Directions and Names of the Winds, on Melissus, Xenophanes, and Gorgias. Probably none of these are by Aristotle himself, but two (On Mechanics and On Indivisible Lines) are very valuable and certainly, like most of the others, products of the Lyceum.

Volume VII. Short discussion of thirty-eight problems. Whether any of them are by Aristotle is more than doubtful, but they serve to illustrate the restless curiosity of his school. The questions are generally better than the answers. For instance: "Why do some people fall asleep the minute they take up a book, while others who are longing to go to sleep wake up if they get a book?"

Volume VIII. Metaphysics.

Volume IX. Ethics (three large treatises).

Volume X. Politics, Economics, and The Constitution of the Athenians.

Volume XI. Rhetoric, and Poetics.

Volume XII. The Fragments of the lost early works.

IO

Aristotle's
Logic

The genius of Aristotle included an unprecedented gift for drawing distinctions, and at the back of all his logical writings lies his recognition of a clear line of demarcation between things and our thought (and speech) about things. The distinction may seem obvious to us. It was not obvious to the generations of thinkers before Aristotle.

The Pythagoreans, for instance, whose contribution to thought was immense, found it difficult to make a distinction between mathematics and physics. They were the first to teach the importance of numbers for the understanding of the universe, but they mistook numbers for things. They called a point One, a line Two, a surface Three, and a solid Four; but their points had bulk, their lines breadth, their surfaces thickness. Thus One, Two, Three, and Four became the stuff of which the universe was built. It was left for Aristotle to draw a clear distinction between physics, the science of things, and mathematics, an abstract science which deals with the number and shape of things.

The same confusion in a more subtle form is observable in Plato's Theory of Ideas. He rightly stressed the universal aspect of things, the Ideas, in accordance with which we group them into classes; and he went beyond the Pythagoreans by including in his Ideas a far greater range of concepts than the mathematical. But when he assigned to the Ideas an independent existence he made a double mistake. He did not clearly understand that the Ideas are an abstraction from things. Instead he turned them into another kind of things, existing side by side with the things they help us to understand. This first mistake involved a second. The Ideas now became for Plato the sole object of scientific knowledge, and, since they existed independently of things, the world of things was left without explanation.

Aristotle saw into the heart of this confusion. He denied a separate existence to the Ideas. The Ideas, according to him, are the intelligible aspect of the world of sensible things. They are the means by which we make order out of the confused world of sensation. To grasp the Ideas is to achieve scientific knowledge of the world of sensible things—the very thing Plato said was impossible.

Just as Aristotle cleared up the Pythagorean confusion between mathematics and physics by his doctrine that mathematics is an abstraction from physical things, so he showed that the Platonic Ideas, which were only a more generalized form of the Pythagorean number theory, are also abstracted from things. This faculty of abstraction was first clearly grasped by Aristotle and is the foundation of his logic. Logic rests on a distinction between things and our mental picture of them. Its sphere is the conceptual world and its purpose is to teach us how to handle concepts. It is thus not strictly a branch of science, but a preliminary training, a *propaedeutic*, to enable the scientist to manipulate concepts without distorting them or drawing false conclusions from them.

Spoken words, Aristotle says, are the symbols of mental experience, just as written words are symbols of spoken words. In logical discourse, we are concerned with the truth or falsity of statements. The question of truth or falsity does not arise in connection with single words but in their combination into sentences. But not every sentence is the concern of the logician. A prayer, for instance, may have a meaning, but this kind of statement is not his concern. He, in his capacity as logician, is interested only in *propositions*. Every proposition must contain two terms, a subject and a predicate, something spoken about and what is said about it. The truth or falsity lies in the relation between the two. It is obvious, then, that the field of application of logic is science. It is when language is used for scientific purposes that it needs the discipline of logic.

But language has other uses. It may be used in order to persuade. This use of language belongs to the art of rhetoric. It may be used to affect the emotions, as in the art of poetry. These are legitimate uses of speech governed by their own rules. But it would be absurd to demand of the orator or the poet that his form of discourse should be subjected to the rigorous demands expected of the scientist, whose concern is truth.

The subject matter of the above paragraph, together with an elaborate analysis of the various types of propositions, is given in the treatise *On Interpretation*, so called because logical discourse is regarded by Aristotle as an interpretation (or symbolic expression) of thought. From it we now turn to the short tract called *Categories*; its purpose is to enumerate the chief headings of thought under which we arrange things. Aristotle fixes the number at ten, a few of which seem much more important than the rest. They are: Substance, Quantity, Quality, Relation, Place, Time, Position, State, Action, Suffering. Here is a sentence to illustrate what he is getting at. There is a man (Substance), alone (Quantity), looking like a doctor (Quality), and wiser than Hippocrates (Relation); he is in the street (Place), now (Time), walking (Position), barefooted (State), toward a surgery, either to treat (Action) a patient or perhaps to be treated (Suffering).

These ten categories suggest all the questions we might ask in order to be informed about a particular subject. The first three are far and away the most important; they are indeed fundamental to all our thinking. As technical terms they come down to us from Aristotle through the medieval Schoolmen. They may serve to illustrate the truth that it is impossible for thought to develop without a parallel development of language. It is not clear who first used the Greek word for substance, but it was Plato who invented the Greek word for quality and Aristotle who invented the Greek word for quantity; and it was Cicero who first translated them all into Latin —*substantia, qualitas,* and *quantitas,* from which our English words come. How could one think scientifically without these words?

The Categories, with which we were dealing before we digressed, are a classification of isolated words. They are names for all the ways in which a thing can be said to be. But Aristotle also provides a classification of a different sort concerned not now with words in isolation, but with the relation of the subject to the predicate in a proposition. These he calls the

Predicables, and they are four in number: Genus, Differentia, Property, and Accident.

Suppose we wish to define the word Man. The Genus would be "animal"; the Differentia would be "rational." As Property (i.e. a permanent attribute found in every perfect specimen of the class) we might put "two-legged" or "warm-blooded." For Accident we have a wide range of choice— "white-skinned," "Greek-speaking," "bald," etc.

We have difficulty when we come to the two long treatises Aristotle called *Analytics*. In these, he expounds his doctrine of the syllogism, which he claims to have invented alone and of which he is obviously proud. The doctrine is elaborate and ingenious in the extreme and historically of great importance. The general idea of the syllogism, of which there are many forms, is to make it possible to deduce from known truths a new valid truth.

For scientific purposes, the most important form of syllogism is the Demonstrative. As a Proposition is built up of Terms, the Subject and the Predicate, so a syllogism is built up of Propositions. The most usual example of the Demonstrative Syllogism, though it does not come from Aristotle himself, is the following:

Proposition 1 (the Major Premise): All men are mortal.
Proposition 2 (the Minor Premise): Socrates is a man.
Proposition 3 (the Conclusion): Therefore Socrates is mortal.

There has been much criticism of the value of this, the fundamental type of syllogism. It is objected that, unless the conclusion were already known, there could be no justification for the Major Premise. If we did not know already that Socrates was mortal, what right have we to say that all men are mortal?

But this is to miss Aristotle's point. Aristotle knew, of course, that the Major Premise rested on an induction. But Aristotle did not think that a valid induction needed a *complete* enumeration, but only a *sufficient* enumeration, of instances. For him, the mind had the capacity of disengaging from the particulars the universal character of the class under investigation. A botanist does not have to examine every plant in the world to produce a true scientific description or definition of each type.

This implies that the world we inhabit is an intelligible as well as a perceptible world, and that we are endowed with minds as well as senses. In the constitution of knowledge both have their part to play. The senses acquaint us with the particulars; the mind penetrates beneath them to the type. Therefore, to go back to our illustration, it is reasonable to say, "All men are mortal," without the obligation of waiting for all men to die. It is reasonable to say, "This man Socrates conforms to the type; he is a man" and to add, "Therefore he will die."

This capacity of the mind to grasp universals is the most fundamental part of Aristotle's theory of cognition. But the syllogism is intended only to be employed for the manipulation of knowledge already gained. It ensures that we handle and apply our knowledge consistently and correctly and deduce from it implications that may have escaped our notice. Aristotle underestimated the amount of new knowledge which was yet to be gained by scientific observation; and he overestimated, in consequence, the information to be won by the manipulation of already existing knowledge.

This manipulation of existing knowledge and the ordering of it into a logically coherent system are often what he has in mind when he speaks of science. But he was vividly aware that this logically coherent system (which, in the enthusiasm of his progressive age, he may be forgiven for supposing to be nearly complete) rested on a foundation not of discursive knowledge but of intuition. We shall conclude our account of his logic with a further discussion of this point.

In the opening paragraphs of his *Metaphysics*, Aristotle gives us a brilliantly perceptive sketch of the stages of knowledge. Animals, he says, are born with the faculty of sensation, and in some, though not in others, sensation gives rise to memory. Such animals can be taught. The animals other than man live by appearances and memories and know little of connected experience. But men live also by art and reasoning. In men, repeated memories produce the capacity for experience, which is the precursor of science and art. These arise when one universal judgment about a class of objects is produced from many notions gained by experience. Such a universal judgment about a class of objects, we may add, is the Idea, Form, or Definition of the thing.

The same ground is gone over again, and more fully, in the last paragraphs of the last book of the *Analytics*. Here Aristotle insists that scientific knowledge through demonstrations (that is, through the demonstrative syllogism) is impossible unless a man has first acquired knowledge of the premises through intuition. To explain what he means by intuition he again goes through the steps by which knowledge of the universals grows in the soul. These are: sense impressions, memory, and experience. When the stage of experience has been reached, says Aristotle, then the universal has at last been stabilized in its entirety in the soul. We can now contrast the universal with the particulars, the One with the Many, and see it as the unifying principle in them all.

To illustrate the process by which the stable, permanent, unchanging concept of the universal is established in the soul out of the confusion of particular impressions, Aristotle uses a striking simile. It is, he says, like the restoration of the original line of battle after a rout. First one man makes a stand, then another and another, until the original formation has been restored. So with the soul. It is so constituted as to be able to stem the rush of sense impressions and gather them into the stability of a general concept.

But the highest generalizations are not reached at once. The first universals grasped are rudimentary. It is necessary that a fresh stand should be made among these rudimentary universals until the higher universals are established. First, for example, we arrive at the concept of a particular species of animal, and only later at the concept of the genus animal. This, in its turn, is but a step toward still higher generalizations.

It is clear, Aristotle concludes, that we get to know the premises of our syllogisms by induction. This induction is of the nature of a direct intuition, not an argument, and the intuition is begun by the senses and completed by the mind. The rudimentary universals are established when sensation gives rise to memory; the more perfect universals are abstracted from the memories by the mind. But the mere emergence of memory rests on the capacity of the sense organs to discriminate one kind of sensation from another.

II

Physics
and Metaphysics

By physics, Aristotle means the science of nature in the broadest and most inclusive sense. In the treatise entitled *Physics*, he treats nature in its most general aspects in eight books. The work *On the Heavens* is concerned with the stars and their motions: Also, for a reason which will be explained presently, it covers the number and nature of the elements. The *Meteorology* is not confined to what we call meteors; its subject is all the changing phenomena of the lower regions of the sky. The biological works, of which we have already spoken, dealing as they do with the flora and fauna of our world, are of course included in the science of nature. So also is the psychology, since the psyche, the life principle, is an integral and inseparable part of all plants and animals. Finally, there is the important treatise *On Coming-to-be and Passing-away*, which is concerned with a special aspect of the subject of change, namely, change of substance, of which we shall have more to say in a moment.

In the *Physics* more than anywhere else, Aristotle is treading in the footprints of the Greek thinkers of the preceding two hundred years. He makes over sixty references to older thinkers. This is characteristic of the birth of the historical sense we have noted in Aristotle, but Aristotle is not here attempting to write a history of early scientific thought. He is conscious of measuring himself against the older thinkers and refers to them mainly in order to disagree with them or, at least, to make clear where he has done better. The major improvement is in the realm of ideas rather than that of observation.

Aristotle feels that the conceptual equipment of the older thinkers was inadequate to their task. Except in biology, where he added an immense mass of new material, he is handling existing information and seeking to transform it by drawing necessary distinctions, defining old concepts more firmly, and introducing new ones. Much of his contribution is of almost inestimable value, but he was not always right, and his errors, being embedded in such an imposing structure, exercised as great an influence as his truths.

Nothing like the vast encyclopedia of knowledge created by him had existed before. For about fifteen hundred years after the *corpus* was first edited in Rome, men prowled around the intellectual edifice he had reared, awed by its majesty, intricacy, and unity of design. To loosen a brick might bring the whole structure down, and it was forbidden to meddle with it.

But it was not Aristotle's fault that he had succeeded so well. In fact his thought, for all its vigor, is, as we have seen and shall see again, tentative, exploratory, and undogmatic. If it was congealed into an orthodoxy, that was not due to him.

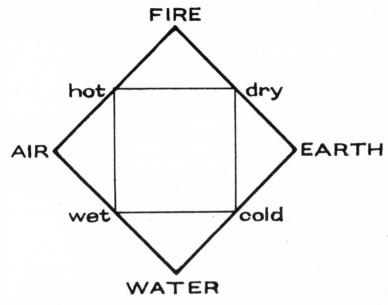

Diagram of Aristotle's scheme of the four elements. The scheme is clever, but not as good as the older atomic theory of Democritus, which Aristotle had dismissed. After Aristotle's death, his two successors, Theophrastus and Strato, severely criticized the scheme.

And if it could be overthrown only by a revolt against its authority, it must be said that the revolutionaries had more in common with the real Aristotle than the authoritarians.

Out of the enormous mass of material in the physical treatises, we cannot in our space do better than select two examples of a notable advance achieved by Aristotle and one of a wrong judgment that long hindered the progress of knowledge.

The older thinkers were principally concerned with two problems—matter and change. To both, Aristotle applied his analytical method.

The concept of change was broken down by him into four distinct notions—Locomotion or change of place, Alteration or change of quality, Expansion and Contraction or change of size, and finally Coming-to-be and Passing-away or change of substance. The first three need no comment, but the fourth introduces us to a brilliant achievement. It amounts in effect to a clear distinction between a physical mixture and a chemical change.

This may be ABC to us, but imagine yourself for a moment at a time when the distinction had not been clearly made. From a physical mixture the ingredients may be separated out in their original form. But what has happened if we mix copper and tin to make bronze or if we make glass out of melted flint and soda? This is a change of *substance*, as Aristotle was quick to see, and he defines its nature in a neat formula of only seven words which require about three times as many to express in English: "Chemical combination is a union of several bodies capable of such combination involving a transformation of the properties of the bodies combined."

This brilliant definition, which is found in the treatise *On Coming-to-be and Passing-away*, rests on a close analysis of the meanings of matter, substance, and property. It was clear to Aristotle that a mere change of Accidents, as when something hot grows cold, is not the same as a change of Properties, as when bronze with its own distinct properties is made out of copper and tin. The latter alone involves a change of Substance. There must, then, argues Aristotle, be something common to copper plus tin and bronze; there must be something which persists after the change of substance. This he called Matter. Matter is the material First Principle of things. It has no qualities in itself but has the potentiality of becoming different Substances when combined with the appropriate Forms.

Matter and Form are thus First Principles or Causes, which underlie the changing world of phenomena. But they are insufficient of themselves to account for the phenomena; we must also allow room for some principle of motion, which initiates the change. This he calls the Efficient Cause.

But we are still without an adequate basis for the analysis of the spectacle of natural things. The observation of nature, and more especially of organic life, discloses to us the fact of the persistence of the species, which has a strangely purposive look. You may feed a chicken, a piglet and a baby on much the same food, but they will go on turning it into chicken, pig, and baby, and when they mature and reproduce themselves they will breed true. Nature, it seems, has her purposes, and intends in one case to produce a fowl, in the second a four-footed animal, and in the third a man, and to go on reproducing them. This observable aspect of nature he called the Final Cause.

Comparing himself, then, with his predecessors, Aristotle claimed that for the most part they understood only the Material Cause and had a glimpse perhaps of the Efficient Cause, but understood nothing of the other two causes—namely, the Formal and the Final Cause. Nature has a certain end (the Final Cause) in view, which she fulfills by stamping on matter a certain specific character (the Formal Cause).

What, then, is the over-all picture of nature that emerges from this analysis? First we must see man himself, the rational animal, standing over against nature. Owing to his possession of Mind and Senses, man is able to appropriate both the sensible and intelligible aspects of nature. This is a process of understanding accomplished cooperatively over the succession of the generations of mankind. It will not be achieved without the setting up of philosophical schools and the preservation of the record. When it is accomplished, it reveals the truth of nature behind the appearances. This turns out to be an undifferentiated Matter, never found by itself but apprehended only by a process of mental abstraction.

A principle of movement in nature, the Efficient Cause, effects a union between Matter and Form. This is a process with many stages and degrees of elaboration. The most simple is the union of Matter with the Forms of the Hot and the Cold and the Dry and the Wet.

The union of these Forms with undifferentiated Matter produces the four elements of Earth, Water, Fire, and Air—Earth being cold and dry, Water cold and wet, Fire hot and dry, Air hot and wet. From these elements are wrought the more elaborate bodies of inorganic and organic nature.

Undifferentiated Matter is a mere potentiality of being. It is not actualized until united with some Form. The union of Matter and Form is an actuality, a realized potentiality, and these actualizations, under the impulse of the Efficient Cause and guided by the purpose implicit in the Formal Cause, achieve a great variety of types of which the highest earthly creature is the rational animal Man.

This, in the barest outline, is the scheme of earthly things. But when we lift our eyes to the heavens we behold a different spectacle. The four elements of which the earthly beings are made—Earth, Water, Fire, and Air—all move naturally in straight lines, Earth and Water having gravity and tending to move down, Fire and Air having levity and tending to move up; and all the things created by the various combinations of these elements are changeable and perishable. But when we look up to the heavens, we find bodies that move in circles and show no signs of change or decay (and these bodies, we remember, were worshiped in the Academy as the highest embodiment of the divine). Could they, then, be made of the same elements as earthly things? Aristotle thought not. He imagined them to be made of a fifth element or essence (our word "quintessence" is derived from this), the natural movement of which is circular. Bodies made of this fifth element, the Ether, are eternal, and it is appropriate that their movement should be circular, for the circle, unlike the straight line, has no beginning and no end.

We have said that it is not easy to date the order of Aristotle's writings, but it is very probable that this celestial scheme, given in the treatise *On the Heavens*, belongs to an early period when the influence of the Academy was very strong upon him. I should think it certain that when Aristotle, in the passage quoted on pages 37–39, was pleading the cause of biological research and contrasting its claims with those of astronomy, it was this theory of the heavens he had in mind. He then gave warning that "speculations about the heavenly bodies can only in the rarest instances be confirmed by direct perception . . . owing to their being out of our reach." And he added that, having already expressed his views on the celestial bodies, he now proposed to do the same for the plants and animals, which, by reason of their nearness to us, "have the advantage from the scientific point of view."

If we are to be just to Aristotle, we must not forget how clear a distinction he himself drew between his speculations on the heavens and his biological researches. It is not his fault that both were accorded an equal authority in later ages; and if Aristotle were alive today and could know how on the one hand his biology is regarded as among the greatest achievements in the whole history of science, while on the other hand his speculative system of the heavens is treated as so much lumber (it had to be cleared out of the way before modern cosmology could begin), he would be fairly entitled to reply: "Well, what of it? I warned you that my system of the

Much simplified diagram of Aristotle's picture of the cosmos—a conception that endured unchanged until the Copernican revolution.

heavens was a piece of speculation which would have to be abandoned if contradicted by observed facts."

Before we leave the subject, it will be instructive to consider how Aristotle's mind worked under two different sets of conditions—first, when he was reduced to speculation owing to the inaccessibility of the heavenly bodies, and next, when he turned to biology, where he was abundantly supplied with facts.

In his cosmology, being reduced to speculation, he argues entirely from imaginary principles. It is appropriate, he thinks, that the universe, because it is divine, should be spherical, because the sphere is the perfect figure. It must rotate in a circle, because circular motion, having no beginning and no end, is eternal. But the center of a rotating body is at rest; therefore the earth, the center of the universe, is at rest.

The earth consists of the four elements, Earth, Water, Air, and Fire. This is the region of change, and the natural movement of these four elements is up or down, which produces a certain intermixture of them. But the region of the eternal and divine begins with the moon. Here the movement is always circular; therefore, the substance of the heavens must be different from those of the earth. Aristotle said it was Ether, and that the natural motion of Ether is in circles at unvarying speed.

In fact, the appearances contradict this requirement, for the planets often show a retarded or even retrograde motion. In the Academy, the erratic motions of the planets had been given a mathematical explanation consistent with the assumption that their true motion was always regular and circular. The apparent movement of each planet was ingeniously explained as the resultant of the motions of a number of spheres, each revolving about a different axis at a special speed of its own. Altogether, over fifty separate circular motions were required to explain the puzzling phenomena. Aristotle inherited this mathematical explanation of the celestial motions from the Academy but converted it into physical terms. The heavens consisted of fifty-five concentric spheres made of the celestial substance, Ether. This had the disastrous consequence of making an absolute separation between celestial and terrestrial mechanics.

The biological studies show an equal ability to construct a system without any corresponding disadvantage. As a general summing up of his researches in this field, Aristotle offers a *scala naturae*, a "ladder of nature," stretching from the lowest to the highest forms of life.

At the lowest rung of the ladder are the creatures that Aristotle supposed to be produced by spontaneous generation, or by budding, or from generative slime. Such are zoophytes and molluscs.

Above them come the insects, whose method of reproduction is by grubs or worms.

On the third rung stand the creatures whose young are produced in the form of eggs. There are many subdivisions of these. They mount all the way up from bloodless marine creatures like *crustacea* to fishes, reptiles, and birds, which are sanguineous.

Above them are the mammals, whose young are born alive. These range from the sea mammals or *cetacea* through the hairy quadrupeds or land mammals to the culmination in man. The superiority of this astonishing system of classification over the cosmology rests, as Aristotle himself pointed out, on the nearness and accessibility of the material on which it was based.

If we still ask why the faulty cosmological construction should have retained its authority till the Renaissance, the answer must again be found in the genius of Aristotle for system-building. The biology and the cosmology are not allowed by him to stand apart as separate structures. He seeks a link between them and finds it in the dependence of the terrestrial upon the celestial phenomena.

It is obvious, and was of course recognized by the Greeks, that the cycle of terrestrial life is dependent on the celestial cycles. Morning and evening, which awaken us and bring us to our rest, depend on the daily revolution of the sun (I am speaking, of course, in terms of Greek cosmology), while the annual progress of the sun through the circle of the ecliptic accounts for the alternation of the seasons, for growth and decay, for the birth of spring, the maturity of summer, the decline of autumn, and the death of winter. The cycle of reproduction—seed, embryo, child, man, seed—repeats the circular movement of the celestial bodies, with the difference that in heaven the individual stars are immortal while on earth immortality is only for the species. Nature makes the things of earth as immortal as by their nature they can be.

The biological world is thus part of the cosmos. And so also is man, in another and special sense. We have already said that Aristotle taught the mortality of the soul but claimed immortality for the mind. Through our minds, we are sharers in the divine, sharers in eternity.

To appreciate Aristotle's meaning, we must follow two trains of thought. First we must return to his doctrine of potentiality and actuality. Unformed Matter, he says, is pure potentiality. Only as Matter acquires Form does it become actual. The more it is informed the more actual it becomes, till at the last, we may speculate, it loses all trace of Matter and becomes Pure Form, or, in other words, is fully actualized. Pure Form, Pure Actuality, would be the highest form of being, would, in short, be God.

If we now follow another train of thought, we may say that everything that moves (using the concept motion in the fullest sense to cover every manifestation of activity, organic or inorganic) is moved from outside itself. Thus, the life cycle of earthly things is caused by the celestial movements.

But whence do they derive their motion? Aristotle argues that, at some point or other in the chain of transmitted mo-

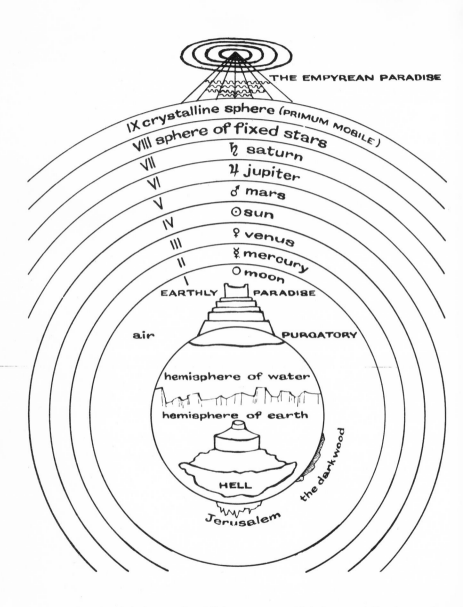

THE EMPYREAN PARADISE

IX crystalline sphere (PRIMUM MOBILE)

VIII sphere of fixed stars

VII   ♄ saturn

VI   ♃ jupiter

V   ♂ mars

IV   ☉ sun

III   ♀ venus

II   ☿ mercury

I   ○ moon

EARTHLY   PARADISE

air   PURGATORY

hemisphere of water

hemisphere of earth

the dark wood

HELL

Jerusalem

Dante's Christian version of the cosmos, which is essentially the same as Aristotle's. (From a design in Singer's *Short History of Ideas*.)

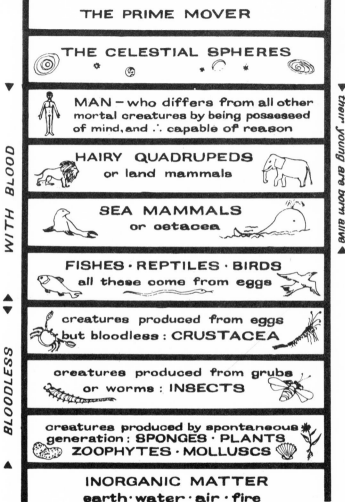

THE PRIME MOVER

THE CELESTIAL SPHERES

MAN — who differs from all other mortal creatures by being possessed of mind, and ∴ capable of reason

HAIRY QUADRUPEDS or land mammals

SEA MAMMALS or cetacea

FISHES · REPTILES · BIRDS all these come from eggs

creatures produced from eggs but bloodless : CRUSTACEA

creatures produced from grubs or worms : INSECTS

creatures produced by spontaneous generation : SPONGES · PLANTS ZOOPHYTES · MOLLUSCS

INORGANIC MATTER earth · water · air · fire

WITH BLOOD

BLOODLESS

their young are born alive

Aristotle's ladder of nature. The diagram is not Aristotle's but is derived from information scattered throughout his biological writings. Essentially correct, it was superseded but not overthrown by Linnaeus in the eighteenth century. It is intended to be not an outline of evolution but simply a plan of living things, from the humblest to the highest forms.

tions, a halt must be called. At the beginning of the chain, there must be an unmoved mover—another name for God. But how does the Unmoved Mover, who is Pure Form, Pure Actuality, contrive to originate and maintain the eternal movement of the heavens?

Such a question admits of an answer only by analogy. Just as an earthly lover is drawn to the beloved, so the cosmos, which in its structure reveals an ascent from pure potentiality to almost pure actuality, is irresistibly drawn toward the only pure actuality there is, namely God, who thus becomes the Unmoved Mover.

But what of man? He too can make the ascent to God by the development of his thinking. The mind, we have seen, is part of the soul and the soul is part of the body, and thinking, which is the activity of the mind, is prompted and sustained by material supplied to it by the bodily senses. But thinking, as it lifts itself out of the sphere of the practical and into the realm of contemplation, becomes more and more abstract, more and more theoretical, more and more pure, more and more concerned with the actuality of Form and less and less encumbered with the material, until at the final and highest stage it emerges as an activity entirely emptied of material content and concerned only with Form; it becomes pure thought, "thinking about thinking." At this stage, its activity is godlike, and the mind has passed from life to eternity.

These speculations, which are scattered here and there through the various writings of the *corpus,* find their chief expression in the *Metaphysics.* This is a collection of essays, obviously composed at various times and attempting to handle the ultimate problems suggested by his researches in various fields.

The ideas expounded in these essays have entered so deeply

into the formation of Christian dogma elaborated in the Middle Ages that we are inevitably led to suppose that Aristotle was a dogmatist and that his *Metaphysics* offers us a closed system of thought.

Nothing could be further from the truth. The very origin of the word metaphysics is proof of this. The fact seems to be that the early editors of the *corpus*, finding a number of essays on difficult points which Aristotle had been forced to leave unsolved in his treatment of the particular sciences, decided to lump them together and to place them "after the physics" (*meta ta physica*), which is all that the word first implied.

But the word metaphysics quickly, and quite legitimately, acquired the sense of an attempt to go further, behind, beyond what had been achieved in the physics. As such, it serves a useful purpose, but it should not be forgotten that the title was first applied to a collection of essays which are exploratory, tentative, and undogmatic to a degree.

This does not rob them of their interest, nor even of their authority. In their combination of ardor and candor, they bring us close to the personality of the man who wrote them. He was a man who shut his eyes to no side of his nature, rational, emotional, or mystical, but acknowledged the obligation to penetrate and permeate every experience with his intellect. He was the man who said of poetry that it was more philosophical than history, because it was more concerned with the hidden pattern of human action than with the surface train of events. He was the man who acknowledged the place of the Mysteries in Greek life by pointing out that their function was to put the initiate through an emotional experience, not to teach him anything. But he was also the man who insisted that in the last event thinking was supreme.

We can now see how difficult it was for later ages to pick and choose among Aristotle's writings, to keep the good and let the bad go. Undogmatic as he was, the exigencies of his nature forced him to forge intellectual links between the different subjects he investigated. The biology, the cosmology, and the psychology are all combined in one philosophical synthesis the like of which had not been known before, and even one who is unable to accept it can well understand how the renovation of his system by the Schoolmen in the Middle Ages should still enjoy with many the title of "the perennial philosophy."

12

Ethics
and Politics

The Aristotelian *corpus* contains three full-scale treatises on ethics—the *Nicomachean Ethics*, the *Eudemian Ethics*, and the *Great Ethics*. It is probable that the first of these is the work of Aristotle himself, and that it got its name either because it was intended to honor his father or to instruct his son, both of whom bore the name Nicomachus. The second, which follows the first very closely, is thought to have been a rehandling of the subject by an admired associate of Aristotle, Eudemus of Rhodes. The third is probably the work of a disciple of the next generation.

Essentially the same doctrine emerges from all three—though the enterprising, exploratory, and masterly quality of Aristotle's thought is, as one might expect, most clearly discernible in the first. It has most attracted the attention of ex-

positors, editors, and translators; it is what is chiefly studied in
the universities; and a reference to the *Ethics* without further
explanation means a reference to this work.

As for politics, the *corpus* offers one large treatise bearing
that name. To this was added at the end of the nineteenth
century, from the sands of Egypt, a fascinating study of *The
Constitution of the Athenians*, which is either from the pen of
Aristotle himself or written under his direction. It was the first
of a great series of political studies, written in the Lyceum but
now lost, describing the constitutions of nearly two hundred
cities, not all of them Greek.

If, in spite of this abundance of material, we treat ethics and
politics together, that is because the circumstances of Greek
life suggest it. In the city-states of Greece, the lives of the citizens were more directly under the control of the state than are
ours. Law, religion, and education were all state business; and,
not unnaturally, ethics was treated as a department of politics.

Toward the end of the *Nicomachean Ethics*, Aristotle
writes, "Youth will not receive a proper ethical training unless
brought up under right laws. To live a temperate and hardy
life is not the choice of most people, especially the young.
Therefore their upbringing and employments should be fixed
by law; what has become customary will not be painful.
Speaking generally, we need laws to cover the whole of life."
This sounds Spartan, perhaps, rather than Athenian; and it is
true that in the crisis of Athenian democracy an exaggerated
admiration for discipline had emerged. But, as we shall see in a
moment, Aristotle cherished an ideal of individual moral autonomy that Sparta could never have tolerated or produced.

We can best understand the background from which the
ethics sprang if we turn to the *Great Ethics*, written by Aristotle's disciple. He briefly describes for us four stages in the

evolution of Greek ethical science. First, he tells us of the abortive attempt of the Pythagoreans to apply their number theory to the elucidation of moral problems.

We have already seen that the Pythagoreans failed to distinguish mathematics from physics, calling a point One, and a line Two, and so on, and trying to build up on this basis a picture of the physical world explicable in terms of numbers. They tried the same with ethics. They identified One with good and Two with evil, and we can feel a sort of sense in their notion. Simplicity and duplicity still combine a numerical with an ethical meaning; and if they called justice Four, well, we talk of a "square deal." But, of course, as a theory of ethics this is pitiable. We can only profit from it by treating it as an example of how desperately difficult it is to take the first steps in any science.

Socrates, according to the writer of the *Great Ethics*, struck out a new line, along which he got further, but also failed. He insisted that virtue is knowledge, that no one willingly does wrong. His mistake was to overemphasize reason and neglect the irrational part of the soul. This made it impossible for him to deal adequately with the passions and to understand the moral, as distinct from the intellectual, side of the soul.

Plato, according to our authority, took the next step. He divided the soul into a rational and an irrational part and assigned appropriate virtues to each. But he got bogged down in his attempt to apply his Ideal theory to the elucidation of ethical science. He sought, and sought in vain, for a definition of the Idea of the Good, thinking that if we knew what Goodness is in itself, in its essential being, the key to morality would be in our hands.

But not only was the quest vain; it was ill-conceived. If Plato had understood the distinctions drawn by Aristotle in the *Categories,* he might have avoided his mistake. It will be remembered that Aristotle defines there ten different meanings of Being. It may be Substance, Quality, Quantity, Relation, Activity, Passivity, and so on. Plato was trying to define the *Substance* of the good. But a science of ethics must determine the good *relative* to man, and this good will not be the same in every case. It will fall now under the category of Quality, now of Quantity, now of Action, and so on.

Aristotle's disciple in the *Great Ethics* makes no scruple of brushing the Platonic Theory of Ideas aside as an outmoded nuisance. Aristotle himself is reluctant to offer disrespect to his old teacher, and we can judge his character by the way he approaches the subject. He feels it necessary to get it out of the way, and this is how he does it in the opening pages of the *Nicomachean Ethics:*

> It is perhaps our duty to raise the topic of the Idea of the Good and ask what it can mean, though the necessity is distasteful because it was friends of ours who introduced the theory. Still we call ourselves philosophers, that is, lovers of wisdom, and where truth is at stake we must not shrink from demolishing theories that have originated among ourselves. Dear as our friends are, the truth is dearer still.

Aristotle then proceeds to develop his own theory, and, in accordance with his usual commonsense procedure, he is ready to take into account the common view. Most men, he observes, if asked for their definition of the highest good, would find it in happiness. Aristotle agrees. "Happiness is manifestly something final and self-sufficient." Honor, pleasure, intellect, and other such goods are indeed chosen for their own sakes, but also with a view to happiness. "But no man chooses happiness with a view to them, nor in fact with a view to any other thing whatsoever." Happiness is thus the highest good. But to call it so without further ado would be to repeat a truism. It is in his definition of happiness that Aristotle's mastery is revealed.

Happiness, he says, *is an activity of the soul according to goodness in a mature person.* Here every word counts. Note at once that happiness is not to be confused with pleasure; it is an activity of the *soul*, not of the body. Then we should note the word *activity*. Happiness is not a passive state. It is achieved by action; and not by any action, but by an activity *in accordance with goodness*. Finally, it is not to be confused with the high spirits of the young. On the contrary, it is to be achieved *by the mature* as the result of a well-spent life. This achievement, as Aristotle fully recognizes, is the result of habituation.

It is often said that the Greeks had too intellectual a view of ethics. But this is not true of Aristotle's school. The writer of the *Great Ethics* says bluntly what is implicit in Aristotle's own position: "It is not the case, as is generally supposed, that reason is the principle and the guide to virtue. This role belongs to the feelings. The first step is to produce an irrational impulse to the right. Then reason takes over and decides what must be done."

Hence Aristotle's emphasis on habituation. He is emphatic that ethical science cannot achieve the rigor demanded in geometry or physics. The first principles in geometry, he says, are grasped by intuition. We just see that the part is smaller than the whole, and so forth. In the natural sciences the first principles are established by induction. But in ethics it is different: There the first principles rest on habituation.

And here is the link between ethics and politics. Only a well-regulated State can provide the conditions in which the

young can acquire the habits on which virtuous living, and
hence happiness, depends. Only a developed philosophy can
supply the theoretical basis for good government. Only political life can assure the leisure in which the philosopher can do
his work. The *polis*, the city-state, which had risen out of
tribal society and superseded it, was the instrument, and the
expression, of a higher form of society.

Aristotle recognized earlier stages of society—the hunting or
food-gathering stage, the pastoral stage, the agricultural stage.
These had provided, at different levels, the economic basis of
life. To many thinkers, in Aristotle's day as later in Rousseau's,
it seemed that these earlier and simpler modes of life had been
ethically superior. Aristotle rejected this view. Political man
was a superior type of man. The earlier modes of society had,
indeed, furnished the means of life; only the city made possible the good life. And since, in Aristotle's philosophy, the true
nature of a thing was only revealed when it had attained its
full development (as the acorn was only a potentiality which
was actualized in the oak), so man was *by nature* a political
animal.

This brilliant paradox, that *man is by nature a political animal*, was the foundation of his theory of politics and his answer to the anarchists and devotees of the simple life.

Like his other treatises, Aristotle's *Politics* evolved slowly.
Here as elsewhere, he first thinks more like Plato and later
acquires an individual tone. As Plato tried to elucidate the
problems of morals by establishing first a universal concept of
the Good, so he tried to solve the political problem by deduc-
ing from first principles the outline of an ideal State. We have
just seen how Aristotle dismissed the Idea of the Good in itself
and founded his ethics on the more closely defined conception

of the good for man. Now, turning to politics, his method is still the same.

Plato, having defined justice as the foundation of the State, and selfishness as the chief obstacle to justice, proceeds by rules and regulations to eliminate selfishness. He puts the control of the City in the hands of a small class of Guardians, and to ensure that they shall not be selfish he deprives them of all the means by which a man normally achieves and expresses any selfhood at all. His Guardians are to have their wives, children, and property in common so as to be uninfluenced by any but communal and public motives.

But this is too much for Aristotle's common sense. Having already decided in his *Ethics* that happiness is the chief good for man, he has no hesitation in dismissing Plato's ideal City on the same score. "The Guardians," the highest class, "must be unhappy," he observes, "being bereft of wives, children, and property. And, if *they* are not happy, who will be? Surely not the exponents of the arts and crafts, nor the mass of manual workers." So much for Plato's *Republic*.

Passing on to the consideration of Plato's later plan in the *Laws*, Aristotle notes with approval that the proposal for community of wives and property has been dropped. But he also notes Plato's persistence in making impossible assumptions in order to secure ideal but impracticable ends. In the *Republic*, Plato had provided for a total of one thousand citizens who were to be free from productive labor and trained only to bear arms; in the *Laws*, he proposes to raise this to five thousand. But Aristotle, whose scientific mind had led him to an acquaintance with the economic realities, objects that five thousand persons to be supported in idleness, together with a still more numerous host of women and attendants, would demand a territory as big as Babylon. As has already been mentioned, the political researches of Aristotle and his colleagues in the Lyceum extended to the study and recording of the constitutions of nearly two hundred States. The temperament that dictated these factual inquiries accounts for the difference in political theory between the dialogues of Plato and the formal treatises of Aristotle.

And, in spite of repetitions and changes of view, arising from its being composed at different periods of his life, Aristotle's *Politics* is a formal treatise of the highest order. After defining the city-state as the highest form of community, it proceeds at once, in marked contrast to Plato, to discuss the family or the household as the basic unit on which the State rests. A complete household, we learn, consists of slaves and freemen. Three relationships are fundamental to its existence: (1) Master and Slave, (2) Husband and Wife, (3) Parent and Child. A fourth topic, the means of gaining a livelihood, is also discussed separately as the material base of the household.

These topics fill the first book. In the second Aristotle gives examples of famous States, three theoretical and three actual. In the theoretical class come the *Republic* and *Laws* of Plato, and the proposals of Phaleas of Chalcedon and Hippodamus of Miletus. Of Plato we have already spoken. Phaleas, his contemporary, thought that landed property should be distributed in equal lots and that all artisans should be publicly owned slaves. Hippodamus, the pioneer of geometrical town-planning, who lived in the fifth century, wanted three classes of citizens —artisans, farmers, and soldiers. The disagreement between Hippodamus and Phaleas on the status of the artisan—was he to be citizen or slave?—illustrates one of the sore points in the thinking of the age.

The three actual States considered are Sparta, Crete, and

Phoenician Carthage. Sparta is condemned for excessive devotion to military training. Crete is dismissed as only an inferior example of the same kind of thing—a military oligarchy whose cities are saved from external enemies only by their island situation. Carthage is frowned upon as a moneyed oligarchy, but is highly praised for its successful management of its internal affairs. The government has never passed into the hands of a tyrant, and the common people remain loyal. This, however, is due to the lucky circumstance of their numerous colonies in other lands. Government-controlled emigration drains off the possible sources of discontent. Of Greek lawgivers, Solon of Athens comes in for the highest praise; a moderate democrat, he conforms to the ideal of which Aristotle on the whole approved.

In his third book, the last with which we have time to deal although there are eight in all, Aristotle has two themes: the definition of the citizen and the classification of types of constitutions.

A citizen is defined as one who shares in the administration of justice and the holding of office. If we ask whether the good citizen is the same as the good man, the answer is yes, in an ideal State. Such a man combines the moral wisdom of the ruler with the humbler virtue of the good subject. Then arises the critical question on which Phaleas and Hippodamus held opposing views. Can mechanics and laborers be citizens; and, if not, what are they? Aristotle finds the question a difficult one but is confident in his solution. The productive labors of the mechanical classes leave them insufficient leisure to acquire any of the wisdom of the ruler. The best type of State will therefore not admit the mechanic to citizenship. The mechanic is a necessary precondition for the State, not an integral part of it. Aristotle, we must not forget, was a defender of slavery.

There remains the discussion of the various types of constitutions. The true end of the *polis* being the good life, it follows that the authority of government should be exercised in the common interest. Any constitution that secures this end is good whether it be rule of the one, the few, or the many. If, on the other hand, it neglects the common good and regards only the selfish interest of the ruling authority, it is bad. Good constitutions, therefore, are Kingship, Aristocracy, and moderate Democracy (which Aristotle calls "Polity"); bad constitutions are Tyranny, Oligarchy, and unrestricted Democracy. So goes the theory, but Aristotle admits that in practice the choice is usually between Oligarchy and Democracy, and that to distinguish these *numerically* as the government of the few and the government of the many is superficial. The choice is really between government of the rich or of the poor, and the upshot is dissension. The two classes profess different theories of justice, the poor holding that men equal in birth should have equal rights, the rich that rights should be distributed proportionally to wealth.

The uneasy balance of these competing interests is revealed by history. In the typical city-state of late antiquity the usual pattern was as follows. The number of citizens was restricted by the exclusion of slaves and aliens. Within these restrictions, the form of the constitution was nominally a democracy. In practice, the higher magistracies and priesthoods remained the monopoly of the rich.

One last topic should be raised before we leave the subject of politics. Astonishment is often expressed that Aristotle, who elaborated his theories when the autonomous city-state was in decline and political power was passing into the hands of emperors or kings, should nevertheless have devised his regulations for small cities. He even showed such a preference for smallness as to suggest that cities should not grow beyond a size that would permit the voice of the orator to be heard by all the citizens assembled in the marketplace.

But surely the answer is plain. It was not for him in the Lyceum to busy himself with the great policy of expansion by military conquest that the Macedonian ruling family, whose faithful servant he was, was putting into effect. He was thoroughly convinced that it was the destiny of the Greeks, if they could achieve political unity, to rule the world. Macedon had imposed this unity on the Greeks. Aristotle's concern was that the innumerable little cities which in his mind's eye he saw as the local centers of administration in a vast empire should be places in which the good life, the philosophic life, could be lived.

13

The Aristotelian Revolution

When Aristotle had been head of the Lyceum for some twelve or thirteen years, there was a temporary revival of the nationalist party, which sought to restore the political autonomy of Athens. Aristotle, the protégé of the Macedonian dynasty, was a natural object of attack. He was charged with impiety, a repetition of the political tactic that seventy years before had brought Socrates to his death. His mother's family had property near Chalcis in Euboea to which he withdrew, and there, after a lapse of a couple of months, he died—of stomach trouble, the tradition says. He was only sixty-two, no great age for a philosopher. But his work had been well and truly done. He had accomplished a revolution in thought that is part of the universal history of mankind.

To suggest the nature of this revolution, we have chosen Werner Jaeger's description of him as "The Founder of Scientific Philosophy." The novelty lies in the combination of the two attitudes. Hegel expressed the same idea by saying that Aristotle was the first great uniter of the particular and the universal, of the fact and the meaning of the fact. He was a great researcher, a great fact-gatherer, in the worlds both of nature and of man. He collected and described biological specimens and political constitutions.

But, for him, knowledge was more than information. His interest was in the interpretation of the facts, the penetration of them by the mind in order to classify them and reveal their interconnections. This process, the discovery of the universal in the particular, he had analyzed and described with astonishing insight.

From the direct encounter with facts there arises memory, the awareness of a similarity between two or more impressions. This awareness of similarity gives rise to the recognition of the common or universal element in the many instances of a repeated experience. This new acquisition, which is more than memory, Aristotle calls Experience. It is the point where the mind of man begins to rise above the level of animal mind. The difference between sensation and thought becomes clear. Things are seen to have not only a perceptual but an intelligible side, and the intelligible aspect is the true object of knowledge. Experience, in this sense, is the basis of all purposeful practical human activity.

But from experience rise two further stages of knowledge. First is art, in the sense in which we speak of the art of building or the healing art. This is the full grasp of the universal element in a particular field of human activity, when the subject matter and the rules of procedure are discovered and organized, and the expert can proceed with confidence to the building of a house or the restoration of health.

And finally we come to science, in Aristotle's use of the term. This is the firm grasp of the universal element in the world of knowledge as a whole. Its aim is not production but contemplation, understanding for the sake of understanding, pure knowledge, which is its own satisfaction and seeks no end beyond itself.

It was to the completion of this temple of philosophy that Aristotle and his school devoted themselves with passionate intensity. That their ideal had in it an element of illusion is, of course, true. But that may be taken for granted. Francis Bacon, who was one of Aristotle's fiercest critics, had his own illusion. He was convinced that he had laid the foundation of the temple of science, that it could be completed in a few generations, and that it could all be contained in a work about six times as large as Pliny's *Natural History*. And just as Bacon's imagination was fired by the transoceanic voyages that had opened up a new world in his age, so Aristotle, fired by the conquests of his pupil Alexander, saw in his mind's eye a world won for philosophy.

In the wake of the victorious armies, he supposed, there would spring up all over the East those little cities of which he had sketched the plan—cities that would provide shelter for the flowering of that highest attainment of nature, the philosopher, the lover of wisdom, the man who could lift his mind by contemplation to share the immortality of the divine being whose mode of existence he defined as pure actuality, thought thinking itself.

We have spoken of Aristotle and his school, and, in estimating the significance of his achievement, the school is almost as important as its founder. Indeed the school was his achieve-

Aristotle. Truly he had earned the title, given him by Dante, of the "master of those who know."

We should consider, very briefly, the survival of his influence after the fall of the Roman Empire, and its role in the formation of the new culture of the Middle Ages. Let us focus first on the Latin West. Christian writers, fighting for the victory of the new religion, were suspicious of Greek learning. For the brilliant Tertullian, the logic of "that wretch Aristotle" was the mother of heresies. St. Augustine, though strongly touched by Platonic influences, was not interested in Greek science. "All learning outside the Bible," he wrote, "if dangerous is there condemned, if helpful is there contained." It was not till the dawn of the sixth century that Latin Christianity began to seek the support of Greek philosophy. Boethius (480–524), author of the famous *Consolation of Philosophy*, had studied in Athens, and he conceived the noble ambition of translating into Latin all the works of Plato and Aristotle. Theodoric, the Ostrogothic King of Italy under whom he held high office, executed him on a charge of treason before he could complete more of his task than the logical works of Aristotle, but their influence was enough to begin an intellectual ferment that culminated in the Scholasticism of the thirteenth century. At about the same time, another Christian scholar, Martianus Capella, succeeded in translating into Latin an encyclopedia of the liberal arts, in which knowledge is classified under seven headings: Grammar, Dialectic, Rhetoric, Geometry, Arithmetic, Astronomy, and Music. As the educational system of the Middle Ages took shape, the first three of these subjects, the *Trivium*, formed what we might call the grammar school stage, while the last four, the *Quadrivium*, constituted the university stage.

Bust of Aristotle, from the Museo Nazionale delle Terme, Rome. (By permisison of the Mansell Collection, London.)

A point of great interest is the relative importance of the two disciplines dialectic (logic) and rhetoric. The function of rhetoric is to persuade, and its role in the Christian scheme of things was the propagation of the Christian view; it was the instrument for the dissemination of established truths. Logic, on the other hand, could appear as a disturbing and innovating force. The purpose of the syllogism was to deduce from two known truths a third truth. It not only systematized but increased the realm of the known. Nobody was more aware of this than the restless and many-sided genius Gerbert, who became Pope Silvester II in 999. He advanced the study of logic immensely by his exposition of the logical treatises of Aristotle and Boethius; yet he upheld the position of rhetoric as the queen of the sciences. Nevertheless, the leaven of logic continued to work strongly in the Christian consciousness of the eleventh and twelfth centuries. Anselm of Canterbury is a case in point. He explicitly appealed to Christians to "stir up their mental powers" in the pursuit of the ideal of "a rational faith."

To the European mind thus stimulated and strengthened by the Aristotelian logic, a fresh infusion of Aristotelian philosophy was now to be administered. To understand how this came about, we must retrace our steps and pursue our inquiries for a moment in a different part of the world.

In the Eastern Empire, where Constantinople withstood the barbarian invaders for a thousand years after the fall of Rome, the Aristotelian texts survived and were studied, and their teachings were, in some instances, improved upon. But the really significant developments took place outside the orbit of Greek civilization and in Oriental tongues. In the Syrian schools of Edessa and Nisibis, the logical treatises of Aristotle were being studied and commented upon as early as the fifth century. When the Arab expansion began, one of the first countries to be overrun was Syria, and the Arabs acquired from the Syrians a taste for Aristotle and for Greek science in general. In Baghdad, in the ninth century, the *Physics* and

Metaphysics of Aristotle and his treatises *On the Heavens* and *On the Soul* were subjects of eager study, along with works of Theophrastus, Plato, Hippocrates, and Galen.

While Constantinople was neglecting the Greek texts and Rome was studying only the logic in Latin, the translators of Baghdad were pouring out Arabic texts that were playing an essential role in the emergence of their new culture. It was the Arab conquest of Spain that restored the full knowledge of Aristotle to the Latin West. In the twelfth century, Gerard of Cremona went to Toledo to study Arabic. Having mastered it, he turned his unquenchable energy to the task of translation into Latin, and he managed, before he died, to endow the West with a library of some sixty or seventy masterpieces of Greek science in medicine, mathematics, and astronomy.

It was bad enough that the Latin West had to go to Toledo in Moorish Spain to learn secular science; it was still worse that Christian theology was also overshadowed from the same quarter. This was mainly due to two men—one a Moslem, the other a Jew—both born in Cordova.

Averroës, a Moslem, had written the best commentaries on almost all the works of Aristotle and, from the height of his intellectual superiority, had given the religion of Islam enhanced authority by reconciling the theology of the Koran with the philosophy of Aristotle. The Jew Maimonides, writing also in Arabic on this occasion, had, in his famous *Guide for the Perplexed*, done the same service for Judaism.

Christianity took up the challenge. Its effort to give system and coherence to the body of Christian dogma culminated in the thirteenth century in the *Summa Theologica* of St. Thomas Aquinas. From our point of view, the interesting thing is that the three world religions Judaism, Christianity, and Islam

but to act, not to be the slaves of circumstances but their masters—we can turn our eyes on few lives that give us greater courage and confidence than that of this man, who sought truth and served it imperturbably amid the many distractions of his day.

Important Dates

B.C.

428	Birth of Plato.
399	Socrates condemned and executed by democratic Athens.
388	Plato founds the Academy and publishes the *Republic*.
384	Birth of Aristotle.
367	Aristotle joins the Academy. Plato's first visit to Syracuse.
361	Plato's second visit to Syracuse.
359	Philip ascends the throne of Macedon.
357	Dion's expedition against Syracuse. Death of Eudemus.
347	Plato dies. Publication of the *Laws*. Aristotle leaves Athens.
347–344	Aristotle at Assos. Marriage.
344–341	Aristotle in Lesbos. Biological researches.
341–336	Aristotle in Macedon as tutor to Alexander. Philip of Macedon completes the subjugation of Greece.
336	Philip assassinated. Alexander succeeds to the throne and is chosen leader of the combined Greek forces against Persia. Aristotle returns to Athens under the protection of the Macedonian viceroy Antipater, and opens the Lyceum.
328	Alexander executes Callisthenes—nephew, pupil, and collaborator of Aristotle.
323	Death of Alexander.
322	Death of Aristotle.

Suggestions for Further Reading

SELECTED PRIMARY SOURCES

Aristotle: Ethics I, Politics I, W. D. Ross (tr.), Chicago: Gateway edition, 1965.

Aristotle: Selections, W. D. Ross (ed.), New York: The Modern Student's Library, C. Scribner's Sons, 1955.

Aristotle's Poetics, S. H. Butcher (tr.), with an introductory essay by F. Ferguson, New York: a Dramabook, Hill and Wang Co., 1965.

The Philosophy of Aristotle, Bambrough, R. (ed.), New York: Mentor Books, 1967.

SECONDARY SOURCES

ALLAN, D. J. *The Philosophy of Aristotle*, London: Oxford University Press, 1952.

ARMSTRONG, A. H. *An Introduction to Ancient Philosophy*, London: Methuen, 1947.

COPLESTON, F. S. J. *A History of Philosophy*, vol. I: *Greece and Rome*, New York: Doubleday, 1946.

GUTHRIE, W. K. C. *The Greek Philosophers: From Thales to Aristotle,* New York: Harper Torchbooks, 1960.

HUBY, P. *Greek Ethics,* New York: St. Martin's Press, 1967.

JAEGER, W. *Aristotle: Fundamentals of the History of His Development,* London: Oxford Paperbacks, 1962.

McKEON, R. *Introduction to Aristotle,* New York: Modern Library, 1947.

RANDALL, J. H., JR. *Aristotle,* New York: Columbia University Press, 1960.

ROSS, W. D. *Aristotle,* New York: Meridian Books, 1959.

TAYLOR, A. E. *Aristotle,* New York: Dover Publications, 1955.

VEATCH, H. B. *Rational Man: A Modern Interpretation of Aristotelian Ethics,* Bloomington: A Midland Book, Indiana University Press, 1966.

Index

Academy (Athens), 4, 6, 9, 10, 17–23, 25–27, 44, 58, 76, 77
Achilles, 52
Adonais (Shelley), 19
Aeschylus, 49
Ajax, 52
Alexander the Great, 11–12, 14–15, 24, 46, 48, 52–56, 57, 100
Alexandria, 58, 102
Amyntas II, 11, 12
Ampelicon, 60
Analytics (Aristotle), 61, 67, 69
Andronicus, 61
Anselm of Canterbury, 105
Antipater, 12, 25, 57
Aquinas, Saint Thomas, 106
Arabs, 105, 106
Asclepiadae, 15
Asclepius, 15
Assos, 26, 28, 31–35, 36, 44, 47, 58, 60
Astronomy, 20, 22–23

Atarneus, 26
Athens, 4, 12, 25, 31, 34, 47, 54, 57, 60, 61, 98
Atomism, 3–4
Attalid dynasty, 60
Attalus, 60
Augustine, Saint, 103
Averroës, 106

Bacon, Francis, 100, 108
Boethius, 103, 105
Baghdad, 105, 106
Barfield, Owen, 44

Callisthenes, 53, 54
Capella, Martianus, 103
Carthage, 95
Categories (Aristotle), 61, 66, 90
Causes, 74
Chalcis, 98, 108
Cicero, 60, 66
City-states, 28, 29, 88, 92, 96, 108

Cleisthenes, 4
Consolation of Philosophy (Bo-
  ethius), 103
Constantinople, 105, 106
Constitution of the Athenians,
  The (Aristotle), 62, 88
Coriscus, 26–28, 60
Corpus of Aristotle, 58–61, 84–85,
  87, 88
Cosmos, 21, 22
Crete, 94–95
Cyprus, 18, 19

Dalton, John, 3
Dante, 103, 107
Darwin, Charles, 40
Delphi, 48
Democritus, 3
Demosthenes, 47
Dialectic, 6
Dicaearchus, 102
Dion, 10
Dionysius II, 10, 49

Economics (Aristotle), 62
Edessa, 105
Efficient Cause, 75, 76
Egypt, 20, 58
Elements of Geometry (Euclid),
  59
Emotions, 50, 51
Epicurus, 61
Erastus, 26–28
Eresos, 28
Ether, 77, 79
Ethics, 87–97
Ethics, (Aristotle), 62, 93
Euboea, 98
Euclid, 59
Eudemian Ethics (Aristotle), 87
Eudemus (Aristotle), 18, 42
Eudemus of Rhodes, 18, 19, 87,
  102
Euripides, 49

Fallacious Refutations (Aristotle),
  61
Final Cause, 40, 75
First Principles, 74
Form, 6, 7, 19, 43, 64, 74, 76, 81,
  90
Fragments, The (Aristotle), 62

Galen, 106
Garden (school of Epicurus), 61
Geometry, 6
Gerard of Cremona, 106
Gerbert, 105
Gods, 20
Great Ethics (Aristotle), 87, 88–
  91
Guide for the Perplexed (Mai-
  monides), 106

Happiness, 90–91
Hegel, Georg W. F., 99
Hephaistion, 52
Hermias, 26–30, 31–32, 47–48, 52,
  54
Herpyllis, 32
Hippocrates, 106
Hippodamus of Miletus, 94, 95
History of Animals, The (Aris-
  totle), 39, 69, 101
History of Plants (Theophrastus),
  101
Homer, 49, 52

Ida, Mount, 26
Ideal Forms, 6, 19
Ideas, 6, 9, 49, 64, 90
Iliad (Homer), 52
Illyrians, 12, 14
In Memoriam (Tennyson), 19

Jaeger, Werner, 9, 99

Kelper, Johannes, 23

"Ladder of nature," 80

Laws (Plato), 52, 93, 94
Lesbos, 28, 31, 36
Linnaeus, Carolus, 40
Logic, 59, 63–70, 104, 105
Logic (Aristotle), 61
Lyceum, 9, 16, 25, 28, 57–62, 94, 97, 98, 101, 102
Lydias River, 12

Macedon, 11, 12, 14, 20, 29, 54, 57, 97
Madariaga y Rojo, Salvador de, 44
Maimonides, 106
Manutius, Aldus, 107
Mathematics, 64
Matter, 74, 76, 81
Menon, 102
Mesopotamia, 20
Metaphysics, 71–86
Metaphysics (Aristotle), 62, 69, 84, 85, 106
Metaphysics (Theophrastus), 101
Meteorology (Aristotle), 61 71
Mind, 44
Museum (Temple of the Muses) of Alexandria, 58, 59, 102
Mytilene, 36, 44

Natural History (Pliny), 100
Neleus, 60
Nichomachean Ethics (Aristotle), 87, 88, 90
Nichomachus (father of Aristotle), 11, 15, 87
Nichomachus (son of Aristotle), 32, 87
Nisibis, 105

Olympic Games, 54
On Coming-to-be and Passing-away (Aristotle), 61, 71, 74
On Indivisible Lines (Aristotle), 62

On Interpretation (Aristotle), 61, 65
On Kingship (Aristotle), 32
On Mechanics (Aristotle), 62
On Motion in Animals (Aristotle), 39, 62
On Philosophy (Aristotle), 32–34
On the Generation of Animals (Aristotle), 39, 62
On the Heavens (Aristotle), 61, 71, 77, 106
On the Parts of Animals (Aristotle), 39, 62
On the Soul (Aristotle), 42, 62, 106

Patroclus, 52
Pella, 11, 12, 14, 31, 46, 47, 48
Pergamum, 60
Peripatetic school, 57
Persia, 46–47
Phaedo (Plato), 17
Phaleas of Chalcedon, 94, 95
Philip II, 12, 14, 15, 24, 31, 46, 47, 54, 56
Physics, 64, 71–86
Physics (Aristotle), 61, 71, 72, 101, 105
Planets, 21, 22, 79
Plato, 4, 6, 7, 9, 10, 11, 17–22, 24–28, 32, 34, 43, 49–52, 59, 64, 66, 89, 90, 92–94, 106
Pliny, 100
Plutarch, 49
Poetics (Aristotle), 52, 62
Poetry, 49, 50, 51
Politics, 87–97
Politics (Aristotle), 28, 31, 62, 92, 94
Protrepticus (Aristotle), 19, 42
Psyche, 23, 41
Psychology, 41–45
Ptolemies, 58, 102
Pyrrha, lagoon of, 36

Pythagoreans, 43, 63, 64, 89
Pythian Games, 53
Pythias, 31, 32, 35

Quadrivium, 103

Renaissance, 107
Republic (Plato), 21, 52, 93, 94
Rhetoric, 104
Rhetoric (Aristotle), 62
Russell, Bertrand, 9

Scala naturae, 80
Scepsis, 26, 28, 60, 61
Scholasticism, 103
Shelley, Percy Bysshe, 19
Short Treatises on Nature (Aristotle), 62
Silvester II, Pope, 105
Socrates, 4–6, 17, 89, 98
Solon, 4, 95
Sophocles, 49
Spain, 106
Sparta, 94–95
Speusippus, 25
Stagira, 11, 12, 24, 54, 56, 108
Stoa, 61
Strato, 101
Sulla, 60

Summa Theologica (Aquinas), 106
Syllogism, 61, 67–70, 105
Syracuse, 9, 10, 27, 49
Syria, 105

Teleology, 39–40
Temple of the Muses (Museum of Alexandria), 102
Tennyson, Alfred, Lord, 19, 43
Tertullian, 103
Theodoric, 103
Theophrastus, 28, 35, 36, 54–56, 58, 60, 61, 101, 102, 106
Theory of Ideas (Plato), 64, 90
Thracians, 12, 14
Toledo, 106
Topics, The (Aristotle), 61
Trivium, 103
Troad, 26, 61

Unmoved Mover, 84

Venice, 107

Wordsworth, William, 23

Xenocrates, 28, 58

Zeno, 61